CW00545302

Galileo's Defence

by

Octavian Paler

Translation by

Cătălina Tomescu

Infarom - PhilScience Press

Târgu Jiu, 2019

Infarom
PhilScience Press
office@infarom.ro
www.press.philscience.org

ISBN: 978-973-1991-96-2

Publisher: **INFAROM**
Author: **Octavian Paler**
Translator: **Cătălina Tomescu**
Corrections editors: **Desislava Walsh**, **CarolAnn Johnson**
Foreword: **Bianca Burţa-Cernat**
Cover theme: *Walking the Line*, watercolour by **George Necula**

Translation from Romanian (original edition published in 1978 by
Cartea Românească).

About the author

Octavian Paler was born 2 July 1926 in Romania, in the village of Lisa, Braşov County.

After receiving a scholarship, he attended the Spiru Haret High School in Bucharest from 1937 to 1944; however, he returned to the Radu Negru High School in Făgăraş for his final year and passed his baccalaureate examination at Sibiu in 1945.

He was admitted to both the Faculty of Literature and Philosophy and the Faculty of Law of the University of Bucharest where he studied from 1945 to 1949. After graduating, Paler was recommended by Tudor Vianu for an assistant professorship in the Department of Aesthetics. He declined that offer, however, and instead accepted employment with the Romanian Radio Broadcasting Company as a special correspondent, later becoming deputy editor-in-chief of the cultural section. After spending a few months in Rome at the end of 1964 as an Agerpres correspondent, Paler took the post of head of the Romanian Television Corporation in 1965, a position which he held until 1968, followed by appointments as deputy general manager of the Romanian Radio Broadcasting Company from 1968 until 1970 and editor-in-chief of the *România liberă* newspaper from 1970 until 1983.

Dismissed in 1983 on political grounds Paler retired the same year citing medical reasons. The Romanian Revolution of 1989, however, saw his return to the public stage with his honorary appointment as the director of *România liberă* and later on of *Cotidianul*.

Octavian Paler first appeared in the press as early as 1958 when some of his poems were published in *Luceafărul*, but his debut as a writer did not come until 1970 with the publication of his first poetry collection titled *Umbra cuvintelor* (*The Shadow of Words*). The works that followed for which he adopted the genres of travel writing and allegory, established his reputation as a major contemporary writer:

Drumuri prin memorie (Memory Roads), 1972

Mitologii subiective (Subjective Mythologies), 1975

Apărarea lui Galilei (Galileo's Defence), 1978; distinguished with the Romanian Academy Award

Scrisori imaginare (Imaginary Letters), 1979

Caminante, 1980; distinguished with the Romanian Writers' Association's Award

Viaţa pe un peron (Life on a Railway Platform), 1981

Polemici cordiale (Cordial Polemics), 1983

Un om norocos (A Lucky Man), 1984

Un muzeu în labirint (A Labyrinth Museum), 1986

Viaţa ca o coridă (Life as a Bullfight), 1987

Don Quijote în est (An Eastern Don Quixote), 1993

Vremea întrebărilor (The Time of Questions), 1995

Aventuri solitare (Solitary Adventures), 1996

Deșertul pentru totdeauna (The Desert, Forever), 2001

Autoportret într-o oglindă spartă (Self-Portrait in a Broken Mirror), 2004

Calomnii mitologice (Mythological Defamations), 2007

In 2005, he was awarded the *Opera Omnia* prize by the Romanian Writers' Association.

Octavian Paler died in Bucharest 7 May 2007.

The confession of a winner

- Foreword -

by Bianca Burța-Cernat

In 1978, when *Cartea Românească* released *Galileo's Defence*, Octavian Paler was already an established and particularly sonorous voice in the Romanian literary world, in spite of his late debut which occurred only in 1970 at the age of 44. This book, the gnomic poetry of *Umbra cuvintelor* (*The Shadow of Words*), is the author's only poetry collection; it is significant, however, as it outlines the essentially lyrical and meditative profile of the future writer of ideas. *Umbra cuvintelor* was followed by the publication of two volumes of subjective notes occasioned by his journeys in Egypt, Greece, and Italy, and in 1975, by a book which proved decisive in drawing the attention to its author. The title of the book was *Mitologii subiective* (*Subjective Mythologies*).

Known prior to the 1970s solely for his work in the media, moving in official circles and being entrusted with high-ranking positions within the Romanian Radio Broadcasting Company and the Romanian Television Corporation, Octavian Paler unexpectedly revealed in these books his essayistic gift of astonishing refinement in terms of both style and ideas. In a world ever more confined where the threats of the July Theses[1] hovered all around, he

---

[1]Translator's note: The July Theses (Romanian, *Tezele din iulie*) is the name given to a speech by Ceaușescu delivered on 6 July 1971 in the manner of

summoned up the mirage of classical culture of Greece, Italy, and Egypt and prompted his readers toward a would-be "escapist" introspection on the periphery of the human condition and beyond the tedium of daily life which, undoubtedly did not encourage creative contemplation. At a time dominated by collectivism and the constant onslaught against privacy, the author of *Subjective Mythologies* made a persuasive plea for individuality and for the values of a life lived in solitude – a message considered subversive by reason of its contemplative structure versus the "teachings" of the Orwellian standardisation. The lesson Octavian Paler was teaching in the 1970s and which turned even more radical in the decade to follow portrayed the morality of solitude as opposed to collectivist promiscuity. The survival solution he suggested was to resist by retreating inwards and embracing the values of self-reflection and escape through Culture. A subject of controversy and often disputed nowadays, this solution seemed convincing, nevertheless, and – with good reason, I believe – to a large number of the intelligentsia who shared this belief even though, in the cold light of day, it was no more than an emergency solution. "In order to escape a concentrationary universe...", noted N. Steinhardt[2] in his *Jurnalul fericirii* (*The Happiness Diary*) – "there is the (mystical) solution of faith". In a concentrationary universe, we can survive

---

Chinese dictators and considered a Stalinist attack on the independence of culture, disobedient intellectuals in particular and free thinking in general.

[2]Translator's note: Nicolae Steinhardt (Nicu-Aurelian Steinhardt) was born near Bucharest in a mixed Jewish-Romanian family on 29 July 1912 and died 29 March 1989. He was a Romanian writer, lawyer, and Christian Orthodox monk known mostly for his work entitled *Jurnalul fericirii* (*The Happiness Diary*).

through culture, suggested Octavian Paler, his view being shared by a great many intellectuals of the communist decades.

Galileo's Defence is one of Paler's most prominent books, being one of those writings which define the author's profile, his dilemmatic disposition; it is also a text faithfully illustrative of the dilemmas of an era. *Galileo's Defence* offers for our reflection the difficulty of having to choose, under severe political repression, between telling the truth loudly and clearly, thus risking absolute annihilation, and officially denying it only to have the chance to reassert it more obliquely and less dangerously, running this time, however, the risk of moral compromise before one's peers and one's own conscience. During the communist years (and I daresay, even for quite some time afterward, more than ten years after the events of 1989[3]), this dilemma did not remain a mere theoretical issue, but evolved into a dramatic existential question. It is for this reason that Octavian Paler's "dialogue on prudence and love" (as the subtitle of the 1978 edition reads) demands to be read as a vivid debate born out of passion and begetting passion rather than as an abstract deployment of arguments intended (only or firstly) to create nothing more than an exquisite spectacle of the mind. Exact in his discourse, gifted with the eloquence of a thinker schooled in the Classical tradition, the author of *Galileo's Defence* assumes also the voice of a romantic in an existentialist quandary, both

---

[3]Translator's note: The events of 1989 in Romania (widely known as the *Romanian Revolution of December 1989*) define a period of violent social unrest which marked the end of more than forty years of communist rule in Romania by the removal from power of dictator Nicolae Ceaușescu, Romania being the last country to dislodge its oppressive Communist regime and the only one to have done so violently.

responsive to his willing heart and sadly torn between conflicting drives.

In addition, *Galileo's Defence* marks a turning point in Octavian Paler's literature of ideas. From then on, his narrative would acquire an Aesopian bent, its subversiveness – thus far implicit – would become more and more apparent for those holding dissenting views, for the silent and the discontented, but equally so for the supporters of the regime – reaching its climax with his almost inconceivable suggestions of *Viaţa pe un peron (Life on a Railway Platform,* 1981) and of *Un om norocos (A Lucky Man,* 1984).

***

The first edition of *Galileo's Defence* enjoyed a positive if noticeably cautious reception, smothered by euphemisms and extensive omissions. Critics from every school and perspective opined on the book, starting with Nicolae Manolescu[4] who set the tone in a punctilious though hardly "brave" article for the *România literară,* followed by Nicolae Balotă[5], Mircea Tomuş, and Ion Vlad,

---

[4]Translator's note: Nicolae Manolescu is a prolific Romanian literary critic born 27 November 1939 in Râmnicu Vâlcea. He is a member of the Romanian Academy and a well-known critical and political voice, particularly since the Revolution of 1989. Manolescu has published over forty volumes of critical works on Romanian literature, the most acclaimed being *Istoria critică a literaturii române (A Critical History of Romanian Literature).*

[5]Translator's note: Nicolae Balotă (26 January 1925, Cluj - 20 August 2014, Nice) was a Romanian essayist, literary critic, historian, former political prisoner, and later a Securitate collaborator. In 1994, his volume *Parisul e o carte (Paris is a Book)* was released, followed in 1998 by *Caietul albastru (The Blue Notebook),* a memorable diaristic essay.

and ending with Ion Dodu Bălan and Emil Manu. The periodicals of the time recorded around twenty articles on *Galileo's Defence* but there may be others as well. The general tone was set by the cautious circumvention of the core issue. Nearly all reviewers were reluctant – and it stands to reason why they were – to read into the recreation of Galileo's controversial destiny something other than a generic representation of an "infelicitous conscience", without any hints as to certain social and/or political determinations. To Nicolae Balotă (*Luceafărul*, issue no. 10/10 March 1979, pp. 1 and 6), Octavian Paler's character – the Galileo tortured by remorse because when forced to choose between Truth and Life, he chose to side with the Inquisition and deny his beliefs – is "a man of the new times" facing an extreme situation. For all its accuracy, however, this statement has the disadvantage of being too equivocal. Nicolae Manolescu was equally non-committal in his critical review *Truth and Life* published in *România literară* (issue no. 52/28 December 1978, p. 9). After an honest description of the book, including a strategic detour via Plato (*Socrates' Defence*), the critic ends his article with a few specific comments on Octavian Paler's literary gift. Among the reviewers of *Galileo's Defence* there were even those who, like the Italianist Alexandru Balaci[6] (*Scânteia*, issue no. 11, 335/31 January 1979, p. 4), performed the extraordinary feat of ignoring the contents of the book by referring mostly to the historical figure of Galileo Galilei and saying next to

---

[6]Translator's note: Alexandru Balaci (12 June 1916, Mehedinți- 7 March 2002, Bucharest) was known as a Romanian Italianist, literary critic, and historian, communist politician, member of the Romanian Academy and during the Communist time, a deputy member of the Central Committee of the Romanian Communist Party.

nothing about Paler's character. By contrast, Virgil Ardeleanu[7] (an active and substantial critic thirty years ago, now fallen into virtual oblivion) chose to make an exception from this "rule" of prudent reviewing and sprinkled his review with a few poisonous double entendres such as when he spoke of a "book open to more than one reading"; he also wrote: "Actually, this book leaves one's mind focused on something else. Not for one moment did I think of the famous scholar while reading it." (*Steaua*, issue no. 2/February 1979, pp. 30-31). It was clear to everyone that, in fact, Galileo Galilei's life was to Octavian Paler's work nothing more than a pretext to present a parable of ethical hesitation in a totalitarian regime. And in this parable, it was quite easy to detect the coordinates of an anxiety-stricken reality.

***

How would *Galileo's Defence* be read today? Is it still relevant to us? Can we possibly like it? How patient would we have to be with this text if we submitted it to an uncompromising (aesthetic) "judgment"?

First of all, we should ask ourselves whether this ethico-philosophical dialogue refers to a "war" which is (also) our own, the readers at the beginning of the third millennium. The books that that carry a particular (and undoubtedly variable) weight in the

---

[7]Translator's note: Virgil Ardeleanu (5 February 1932, Târgu Mureş, Romania - 2006, Cluj-Napoca, Romania) was a Romanian literary critic specialising in Romanian contemporary prose. He was a choleric, keen, and concise literary voice, totally lacking any falseness, prompting many fierce reactions at the time. He is known mostly for his work published in 1966, *Însemnări despre proză* (*Notes on prose*).

history of literature are the ones that can, among other things, meet a double demand: one exacted by their time and the other by the staying power they possess. In other words, such books give, even indirectly, an eloquent expression of the times in which they originated and whose questions engendered them, and at the same time fully retain their ability to fire out questions and present valid issues for consideration outside the constraints of a particular moment in history. Put differently, the books which never miss the mark are those that manage to strike the right balance between the raw immediacy of personal experience and the indispensable intuition of all that we share as humans. Viewed from this perspective, while *Galileo's Defence* remains a documentary of an era which is not yet obsolete, an X-ray of the totalitarian neurosis of a *particular* time and place, it is just as much a text of protean potential, prone to recontextualization.

Although the fall of communism occurred relatively recently, and so the concentrationary universe depicted in the 1978 edition of Octavian Paler's book will have impacted the reader of the new millennium (however heavy the "mark of the present" may supposedly weigh upon those educated after 1990), there is yet another reason to consider *Galileo's Defence* to be a book abreast of its time. It rests in the very essence of the book's topic, the illustration of a conflict which still causes a stir: on one side of the barricade, the would-be heroes who could not rise to the occasion; on the other, the ones who glare across accusatorily because their confidence in the value of "heroism" has been violated. At a time when we are witnesses to trials for treason brought against intellectuals who made a pact with the communist regime (for various reasons – and the discussion ought to be as moderate as possible at this point), *Galileo's Defence* cannot be otherwise but

13

contemporary. It is a confession, a cry, a plea for a sensible, unbiased and sincere judgment. The embodiment of an ethical dilemma, the book does not offer any ultimate answers to the questions raised: How guilty is the intellectual who cannot become a martyr? Who is entitled to pass judgment? How efficient is sacrifice for actual existence (in manifest disagreement with the theories on truth, justice, and duty)?

***

When the book was republished in 1999 (by *Albatros* Publishing House), Paler made a few changes. Before pinpointing them, it should be said that the departure from the *editio princeps* was not the outcome of any discrepancy of ideas triggered by the shift from communist censure to freedom of expression. The books written before 1989, the present one included, cannot even remotely – and despite a thorough (re)reading – be suspected of any ideological compromise. If certain "renunciations" can be attributed to Octavian Paler – something completely unavoidable by anyone working in the media of the time – his work is, for all that, beyond reproach. After all, Galileo's argument as constructed in Paler's book, appeals not only to the human comprehension of the reader, a potential prosecutor, but also to reason: "Saving my life meant saving the possibility of continuing my work, of writing new books. Would they rather I let myself be reduced to ashes? I defended my life, and along with it, my chance to see my work through. I don't believe I've made a mistake." Or: "[...] given that life is the only real philosophical question, I hereby agree to recant my views on the solar system. But this shall be the one and only reason why I'd agree to do it."

In the first version of the book (adapted for radio theatre in 1979 by Constantin Vişan[8]), at the end of a debate dominated by the intransigence of his own conscience, Galileo allows himself to be persuaded of his mistake, and the book is given a "heroic" closure with a Galileo willing to recant his compromise with the Inquisition and preparing to walk up the steps of the stake. But a heroic Galileo, a Galileo turned into a zealot for the sake of an abstract truth looks somewhat inhuman. Octavian Paler reworked the text in the 1990s in an attempt to humanize his character. The new version of the dialogue proposes an open ending – more relaxed and consequently more authentic – which gives the reader the freedom to draw their own conclusions, and the character the freedom to act according to his own nature. We now know that one of the literary sources of *Galileo's Defence* (in addition to the much cited Platonian dialogue) was *The Life of Galileo*, a play by B. Brecht[9] written at the end of the 1930s. Both works show a Galileo who honestly assumes his weaknesses, not only his great projects which he chooses to continue covertly, but more safely, when major obstacles would stand in his way. The arguments raised in defence

---

[8]*Translator's note:* Constantin Vişan (18 April 1930, Aiorman, Kaliakra, Bulgaria - 22 September 2014, Romania) was in the service of the Romanian Radio Broadcasting Company and of the Romanian Television Corporation for nearly half a decade, running the literary and artistic departments of these institutions for a period of time and nurturing generations of radio people.

[9]*Translator's note:* Berthold Brecht born Eugen Berthold Friedrich Brecht (10 February 1898, Augsburg – 14 August 1956, Berlin) was a German author, art theorist and famous public figure whose artistic theories and revolutionary views on theatre gained him influence and notoriety worldwide.

by both Brecht's and Paler's Galileo, are very similar: that their Work justifies petty cowardice, and that after all, recognition of one's own vulnerability is a form of lucidity and honesty; that what Truth asks of those who profess it is not to die for it but to go on living; that setting oneself up as a prosecutor when one has never had to recant anything simply by virtue of never having faced the stake is unjust.

Unlike Brecht's play, however, in which the accused Galileo has the final say and the accuser (a former disciple of his) is given counterarguments which at times appear weak, in Octavian Paler's dialogue, the lines of Galileo's unknown interlocutor are often as lashing (and sowing methodical, prolific doubt) as the "defencive" statements of the one standing trial. For instance:

"Galileo, the goal of any inquisition is to create two realities. One seen, the other one unseen. The control over visible reality offers the Inquisition control over invisible reality as well. Thus, people get used to believing that it doesn't matter what one thinks. What matters is what one says. So everyone says what they are required to say and what they believe they have to say if they want to save their skin. And if at first, they are disgusted with it, afterwards it becomes a habit. Then, many are driven into it by interest. The outcome? I believe you know it. You've seen it. Little by little we all realise that everyone around is lying and pretending and not taking any chances. And so, we wonder: why should I act differently? The very idea of conducting oneself with honesty in a world where hypocrisy alone pays off has come to sound quite insane, a veritable folly."

The first edition of *Galileo's Defence* and even more so its second 1997 edition (as well as the present one), is a polyphonic text of exquisitely mobile ideas, deconstructing the dramatized debate down to the tiniest detail. Subtlety is what chains each point of view to its opposite, and both conflicting voices share the same resonance.

The second edition of the book not only underwent noticeable adjustments (the seventy-three episodes were reduced to fifty-three as the author may have sensed that certain passages, in their repetitiveness, curbed the dynamism of the debate) but also in-depth textual resizing. Apart from rephrasing certain passages – more often than not by abridging them - the dialogue between Galileo and his "mysterious" visitor was restructured by "breaking" longer replies into shorter ones, thus restoring the balance between the two forces. While initially Galileo was given a much bigger part in the conversation, he was now increasingly forced to surrender his right to speak. As a result, the discussion assumes a more animated and natural character. An element of major significance is the transformation of Galileo's accuser from a quasi-impersonal voice into a full-fledged character. While in the 1978 text, Galileo's opponent could be easily interpreted – as he was indeed – as a simple metaphor of the divided conscience of a character eaten up with remorse, a hostile and spectral alter ego of the one who betrayed himself, the new version of the book portrayed this interlocutor as a visitor in the flesh who calls on Galileo at his house in Arcetri (near Florence) where the latter had withdrawn in complete solitude accompanied only by cypresses, after his abjuration in 1633…. Now the visitor is given the identity of a historian who himself had consented to serve the Inquisition by writing Torquemada's[10] biography. He even suggests on a few occasions that he "might be" an Inquisition collaborator purposely sent out to take the measure of the ostracized scholar. ("You might have reasons to believe that I'm a spy sent out by the Inquisition.") The accuser, as a spokesperson for all those disheartened by Galileo's gesture, slowly assumes the role of a confessor and eventually offers his own confession to the accused. Paler inserts a further episode which is difficult to avow from the biography of the character posing as prosecutor: despite mitigating circumstances, he is indirectly to blame on account of his cowardice (the same weakness imputed to his interlocutor), for the death of his fiancée, fallen prey to the accusations of the Inquisition.

Undoubtedly, there are other similar changes, all converging towards a more human and, where possible, a more personal expression of this "philosophical dialogue". Furthermore, the conflict is subject to a considerable shift from within towards the boisterous reality of the agora, filled with its accusatory discourses, often valid but nevertheless unfair and only pretending to seek justice.

The reader of this book of paedeutic substance comes to understand why Galileo's dilemma is "the dilemma of everyone who is afraid. Or who will one day grow to know fear, having

---

[10]Translator's note: Torquemada born Tomas de Torquemada (14 October 1420, Valladolid, the Kingdom of Castile - 16 September 1498, Avila, Spain) was a Castilian Dominican friar and the first Grand Inquisitor of the Spanish Inquisition responsible for the execution of nearly 2,000 people accused of heresy and for the expulsion from Spain of thousands of people of Muslim and Jewish descent.

deluded themselves into thinking that they would never know what it is to be threatened."

"The greatest joy after being in love is confessing one's love"

(*The Journals of André Gide*)

I hereby "recant" the version of this "dialogue" published in 1978 not because there would be anything I wish to recant there. Whatever I believed during the summer I wrote it still holds true to this day. Something else caused me to review "Galileo's Defence", hastily, yet substantially, omitting some chapters and adding others. When I received the offer to have the book edited afresh, I reread the text of Galileo's abjuration which, as you may know, begins as follows: "I, Galileo Galilei, being in the seventieth year of my life…." That summer when I "defended" him, I was exactly in the fiftieth year of my life. Now I am in my seventieth. At the time, "life" presented itself to me only as an unquestionable value. In the meantime, I came to realise that despair is a form of love and that any great love has something tragic lying underneath. And thus I understood, at the age of seventy, that a sunny day may, at times, be worth more than heroism. With this in mind, I prepared this new version of "Galileo's Defence".

Other than that, I trust and hope that anyone who has lived through what we have will need no further explanation in order to understand that I did not imagine such a "dialogue" or to unearth the "Galileo Galilei Case" from the archives or to engage in any philosophical debate.

I

"Galileo, I don't know what happened there before the court of the Inquisition. You may have been forced to recant. And after all, this is a matter of concern to you alone."

"What are the people saying?"

"Things you already know. Some say you've been wise to avoid the stake; others claim you hold your body dearer than your ideas."

"No one knows the price I had to pay for those moments."

"Couldn't you have had it otherwise? Not to recant. . . ."

"As I've told you before, my heart did not recant anything."

"Well, it did, it recanted what it had believed in."

"But the earth spins on, doesn't it? Even though the Inquisition will not have it. . . .?"

"That's true indeed, but you cannot take any credit for that."

"Look, I'll tell you how it happened. Clad in their purple robes, they sat in their high thrones and once they had stopped talking, nothing else could be heard around; the hall sank into an awkward silence. Never before had I imagined how difficult it could be to endure a silence that nails you to a place from which you desperately want to flee. I felt I was suffocating, and a sense of nausea came over me. *Why would they possibly care about what the earth and the sun look like?* I asked myself. What are the earth and the sun to them? I had to tell them something, anything, just so I could get out of there as soon as possible . . . never have to look at them again. They were staring at me with such empty, glacial, ruthless eyes."

"Inquisitors cannot smile."

"By the end of it I had almost grown deaf to their questions. I was solely obsessed with the look in their eyes. Empty, full of cruelty. . . ."

"… uniform cruelty. . . ."

"… and what is more, full of coldness. Their eyes were riveted on me as if I were some sort of object. It was this that made them unbearable. I had never felt more annihilated in my life. I was no longer myself. I had been turned into something of no worth. A nothing they could easily and smoothly do away with."

"Nevertheless, they needed you to be seen down on your knees."

"It was as though I had been hit in the stomach. I was dizzy, I felt sick and I was afraid I might throw up. Then, I told myself that I had to get away before I had made a complete spectacle of myself."

"You were quick to recant."

"I'm convinced that I was put to every possible indignity there."

"Don't say that, Galileo. You don't know what the stake is."

"One of the inquisitors was watching my hands incessantly as though my entire being seemed of no interest to him, except for my fingers."

"He may have been wondering whether they wouldn't look better crushed."

"Many thoughts were going through my mind at the time. I thought of these cypresses, too, and that I might never get to see them again. And of the wheat fields where I would lie idly in the shadow of a sweetbriar, subdued by the scent of ripe wheat ears and heavy sun-soaked grass. For a second, I was overcome by a wild desire to roll down a ridge of thistles in full bloom in the sunlight like I used to do in the days of old …You see, all my memories then sided with the Inquisition. They drove me to recanting. Can you understand that my entire past was pushing me to it? Because each memory that I recalled was filled with sunlight."

"It's the fear of death, Galileo. As simple as that".

"This was how my memory forced me not to stand up to the inquisitors anymore. It might have settled it all… Well, one thing is clear: I am neither strong enough nor lonely enough to follow in the wake of the martyrs."

"Let's leave the martyrs out of it for now. They abided by other rules, even though they too had their memories to face".

"I suppose my efforts to explain myself are worthless. Everyone has their own reasons. But perhaps we should talk about summer instead."

"Forgive me, Galileo, I didn't mean to offend you."

"Besides, you're far too young to understand why I always keep looking back."

"Even so, I've learnt that in order to be a fair judge, one has to take a step back . . . ."

"Where memories are concerned, we are the gods' equals. Not even they can change them . . . . That which has happened already cannot be undone, either by their power or that of destiny. But I believe I am amongst those who feel the need to harp on about certain things in their life even if they cannot change anything."

"You feel the need to explain yourself."

"Not to explain, but to defend myself from gossip. I've never liked being made to choose, and all of a sudden, I was forced to make a choice between the stake and my life. How could I have ever chosen the stake? What can something which takes everything away from me possibly have to offer me in return?"

"Loyalty to your ideas, some might say."

"I am still faithful to my heart."

"Why do you pit your heart against your ideas, Galileo?"

"Why? Because the heart has its reasons. And besides, you don't know how I get through the nights.... Perhaps I ought to tell you then that I envy those whose sleep is without dreams, whose nights are serene and empty."

"You speak as if your fear has survived to this day."

"Daylight keeps me apart from the inquisitors by putting between us everything that surrounds me. Neither their intentions nor their questions can touch me anymore. What comes to my defence is the light, the summer, the fruit. But when the night falls, I am defenceless. Then snakes begin squirming in my sleep. And although I don't believe you can imagine what I'm going through, I'll tell you a story. A couple of years ago, a forester captured some vipers to sell them for their venom. He put them into a sack, tied it up tightly at one end and shoved it under the bed where it was to stay until the following morning. Then he went to bed. When he woke up, he was horrified to see the snakes snuggled asleep right next to him. Perhaps, the knot had not been so tight after all."

"Dreadful nightmare."

"The story is as true as they come."

"And how did he get out of it?"

"In sheer terror, he understood that if he made a single, move the vipers would bite him. So he lay stock still in his bed, not a twitch, not a move, just waiting. Fortunately, his wife came by the cabin in the morning as was her habit and entered the room without slamming the door. She wanted to speak to him, but with a look of terror in his eyes, he made her aware of the snakes. The woman advanced gently, saw what had happened, boiled some milk, and put it in a pot on the floor. Picking up the scent of hot milk, the vipers stirred and left the bed one after another."

"Terrible ordeal."

"Well, one night I dreamt I was the forester. Only this time it was an inquisitor who came by my cabin. He was silent, and he was staring at me. He sat down and suddenly I noticed that the chair he was sitting on resembled an inquisitorial throne. He took out some candles, put them on the table, and lit them. . . . His hand was tiny. . . . Have you ever noticed that many inquisitors have really tiny hands?"

"That is because they don't torture others with their own hands."

"The whole time he paid no attention to me. He walked quietly about the room as if he were all alone. My existence seemed immaterial to him. Then suddenly he turned towards me. Terror-stricken, I waited for his voice to awaken the vipers . . . ."

"What happened next?"

"He moved only his lips, but I could read perfectly what he meant. He asked me: 'Do you recant? Do you still believe the earth is spinning?' I watched him in dismay, too scared to utter a word. 'If you refuse to recant, I will speak out loud and the vipers will wake up,' he continued. He paused and then added with a smirk on his face, 'And if you recant, you will wake up the vipers yourself.' I realised that no matter what I chose, ultimately the end would be the same.' The inquisitor gave me a scornful look. His lips moved again: 'Do you see now? You have no way out. So, when the candles have burnt down, my voice will regain its sound and you shall be lost.' That instant I cried out, but I don't remember what I said. I woke up soaked in sweat. . . . Perhaps, just like the forester, I went through it all."

"I'll say it again, Galileo, you don't know what the stake is. And you must accept that everything was just the way you remember it."

"I know that. But there was a moment then when I stopped thinking about the questions I was asked. My only fear was that I'd throw up."

"Because you were frightened?"

"And disgusted. For this too I recanted. So that I could get out, breathe in some fresh air. I felt I couldn't bear it any longer. Never had I loved more the afternoon light! I wanted to see it as soon as possible."

"That's the reason you're strolling all alone now amongst cypresses?"

"One can tell, judging by your words, that you've never faced the inquisitors. Their eyes are as cold as ice. When they look at you, they stain you with death."

"Were I to play the devil's advocate here, I would point out to you that just as the state needs the police in order to protect us from robbers, the Church too feels bound to defend itself from heretics. Jesus Christ Himself banished the Pharisees from the temple, didn't he?"

"It is not the same thing. And besides, God doesn't need a praetorian guard."

"I agree, Galileo. That is precisely why I wish to stick to what the people say and to my own doubts."

"All right, then . . . As you wish."

II

"People say you didn't rise to the occasion, Galileo."

"Can you rise to the occasion when you are given no choice?"

"But you had a choice."

"Between the stake and my life?"

"You can't deny that some people found the strength to choose the stake."

"No, I can't, but I don't think it reasonable to be put in a position to prove such strength, either. Do you think that since I failed to prove it, I do deserve to be the object of their scorn?"

"Where's your selfishness now?"

"What do you mean?"

"Since in your reckoning you've placed life above and beyond everything else, I suppose you shouldn't concern yourself with what people think about you."

"I may not be quite a misanthrope yet, but I may still become one if I keep going over what I've been through these past few years."

"But you talk only about that which pleads your innocence, Galileo."

"Does that surprise you? I once met a man who unlearned the habit of smiling. He had bad teeth, many of which had fallen out, and as he avoided opening his mouth more than necessary, every utterance became a torture of articulation. Whenever he felt like laughing, he put his lips together so as not to let his bare gums show and he shook with laughter, his lips slightly parted. Certainly, all these gesticulations require continuous self-supervision. He had to keep his natural impulse to laugh under control. And I am sure this kind of pressure did not stay just on the surface. The fear of revealing his toothless mouth curbed his freedom in more ways than one. And perhaps what was worse was that he came to hate those who laugh at the top of their voice."

"Why are you telling me all this?"

"I'm not sure myself. I'm just saying whatever comes to mind . . . . I dreamt of a city which had everything it needed: buildings, towers, horologes, markets. But there was one thing missing: its past. The horologes refused to measure anything else but the present moment. Their sounds were devoid of any echo. The elderly faced their death in solitude amongst trees and walls without shadows. Because nothing in this city cast a trace of a shadow – not the wall, not the trees, not even the people. The sun pierced through things as if everything were made of glass. And meanwhile, an inquisitor was telling the crowds: *We must burn a few people at the stake and bury others alive. Only then shall we have something to remember!* 'No,' I cried, 'that's not the kind of past we need', whereat the inquisitor gave me a scornful look: *Most certainly*, he said, *I've heard this voice before. It belongs to someone who recanted.* All eyes were upon me. Then they resumed their discussion ignoring my presence. Only one of them kept sizing me up. And I heard him whisper, *Why not start with him? Compared to us he seems so full of past . . . .*"

"I can see that the prospect of becoming a martyr terrifies you even in your sleep, Galileo."

"It does indeed. You see, I don't think the world needs martyrs. Why do we need examples of how to die? Wouldn't it be better to have examples of how to live?"

"Nonetheless, martyrs testified to how one's death can be turned into immortality. You may not be willing to accept it, Galileo, that martyrs may have failed to make the most of their lives, but they most definitely have not failed to make the most of their deaths. It's simply that you are obsessed with the terror you have been put through."

III

"How strange! Ana told me almost the same thing."

"Who's Ana?"

"A woman I've been dreaming of for some time but whom I've never actually met. I gave her a name for convenience sake."

"What does she look like?"

"I've never seen her face. There has always been something in the way, either the sun or the darkness, which has kept me from seeing her face. "

"And what does she tell you?"

"The same thing she said the first time we talked. That she was here to bring me peace. Her hair was silky soft and fair, reaching all the way down to her knees. A few locks covered her cheek. Her words came out slowly, evenly, as if carried on the wind. *Put your head on my shoulder*, she said, *and you'll be well. You will be rid of whatever it is you wish to leave behind*. I did as she told me. Her shoulder was white, as soft as grass, and once I'd leaned my forehead against it, I no longer knew who I was. I stayed like that for quite a long while. Ana's hair had the scent of wind and night, and I felt that I was one with the cypresses rustling around or the pine trees upon the hill in the distance. 'Who am I?' I asked her. And although I wasn't really concerned with the answer, I was rather intrigued by it. *You're a man chased by a stake*, she said. 'What do you mean chased by a stake? I don't understand. Stakes are motionless; they burn until they've turned everything into ashes.' *Sometimes they don't. Sometimes they chase people like beasts do. If you lift your cheek off my shoulder, you'll see that I am right*. I listened to her and glanced around. But I could see nothing. There was no fire burning in the damp, black night still marked by the rain which had fallen the night before. Without making the slightest movement, like a ghost of the grasses, Ana waited. 'There's no stake in the woods', I said. *Not in the woods, Galileo*, she replied. *Look inside yourself. In fact, this is what's torturing you. You're carrying in your heart a wound that won't heal*."

IV

"And that's what I have to live through every single night. But then again, every single morning, I'm grateful to be alive. Old and poor-sighted as I am, I still enjoy watching the sky brightening in the morning and the dew shining on the cypresses at sunrise. The first light of day on these hills is heartbreakingly beautiful to watch and I could never have enough of all this which otherwise I would have lost. Whatever extols life pushes me further away from the stake."

"You're just happy to be free again, that's all."

"I'm happy to be alive."

"But you recanted a truth."

"I've got plenty of time to spread this truth into the world, now that I'm alive. And I don't see why I should be ashamed to admit that I do fear death and that I do love these summer skies so passionately that it scares me I might lose them . . . . As a matter of fact, I'd do better to talk of 'love' instead of 'fear'. Then everything might become clearer, or at least, you'd see that my words are by no means deceitful. Each and every second the earth tells us the same thing: death is ruthless. And if only we could grasp this message, stakes would never be right."

"It's odd to hear you speak of happiness, now of all times."

"Why do you find it odd? To Epicurus, happiness was to be like stones, insensitive to pain. But I for one am convinced that happiness requires a soul capable of loving light and objects alike. "

"You seem to have forgotten about the truth again."

"But the objects and the light – aren't they full of truth? Take a closer look at these stones, a remnant of a deserted monastery overgrown with grass. The feeling I nurture before them is 'heretical' because I cannot hate the grass which buries them."

"It seems like gratitude, not love, to me."

"Well, yes, I am grateful to be alive and desperate when I think that there will come a summer when I won't see the cypresses go darker in the noon light. But this is quite natural at my age, isn't it? There's pain in everything I love now, because everything beautiful carries with it the sense of the approaching end. Perhaps this is what true love looks like. *Enjoy this evanescent gift*, a voice is shouting inside. Because evanescent gifts are all we have. Where do we come from? Where are we heading for? We are heading nowhere. Here is all there is. What happens here is all that matters. When I told Ana about this, she spoke of Alexander the Great again."

"Alexander the Great?"

"She always speaks of him, and she feels the need to talk about the sands of the East . . . . Perhaps this is where she comes from . . . . This time, however, it didn't have anything to do with what I had said. 'Why do you keep mentioning Alexander to me?' I asked her. *Because just as he used to carry the Iliad encased in a small golden chest, so you carry your fear inside you. He wished to conquer the world out of jealousy towards Achilles; you wish to conquer it in spite of what you're carrying within you.* 'I do not wish to make any conquests. I merely want to live like a normal human being', I told her. *Why do you need me and the cypresses then?* I could feel her vegetal hair touching my cheek. And I think my answer was somewhat foolish: 'Because you're kind.' We both kept silent for a while. Then, in the same slightly husky and detached voice which sounded like the rustle of the cypresses, she murmured something utterly unrelated to what we had been discussing before: *Sometimes people squander love on worthless things.* 'Nothing is worthless if it is what one loves', I retorted, and when I saw her leaving without a word I wondered whether I had been uncivil."

"Could it be you've fallen in love perhaps?"

"With whom?"

"With her."

"Good God, the thoughts you're thinking! Ana is just like the wind. And besides, haven't you understood by now that love to me is something to oppose fear? As soon as I see the sky, the cypresses, the sunny grass, I feel a bitter passion burning within. Whatever I cannot touch now will be lost to me forever. The only real paradises are the ones in which we have rambled, we have loved and been grateful. This is what I think about every morning when the light runs down the bark of the cypresses."

"Galileo, do you think that all you have to do is reach out to happiness? And that happiness will be right there where you've held out your hand to reach for it?"

"It will certainly be where my unfaltering belief in it says it is. Because the peace I need is one that is my own. There might come perhaps an age or a time when all this will be settled, but what I know for certain right now is that what these hills and what summer mean to me I couldn't have found anywhere else. Mine is a world without saints."

"Or heroes either."

V

"This is what people expected from me? To be a hero?"

"It depends on the meaning you assign to the word, Galileo. If it means your failure to say that the earth does not spin when you know for a fact that it does, well then, yes, this is what they expected."

"And I proved myself a disappointment to them."

"I'm afraid you have. Many had put their faith in you."

"And I should have died to keep their respect? Alive and breathing, I'm not worth a fig?"

"They would have wanted you to be brave."

"I for one don't see how dancing on a barrel of gunpowder could ever constitute proof of valour. You can just as well dance one step further away from it."

"You sound quite proud of your prudence, Galileo."

"I'm not proud, but I'm not ashamed of it either. Stakes could never beget anything good. Saving my life meant saving the possibility of continuing my work, of writing new books. Would they rather I let myself be reduced to ashes? I defended my life and along with it my chance to see my work through. I don't believe I've made a mistake."

"Don't you have any doubts gnawing away at the back of your mind?"

"As far as this is concerned no, I don't. Remember what they say about how Marsilio Ficino would start his classes."

"Instead of 'Beloved brothers in Christ' he would say 'Beloved brothers in Plato'. "

"Well, now I'd say: 'Beloved brothers in life'."

"You don't seem to set much store by holiness, do you?"

"To tell you the truth, I actually don't understand it. I've always thought the only promises I can rely on are the ones pertaining to this life. Look at the cypresses. When the midday light makes them grow darker, they take on the appearance of monks, but there is no holiness that I can sense when I stand before them. Or at best, they remind me of a saint, his arms full of fruit and grass bathed in summer scents."

"What you're saying now is pure heresy."

"I would have well deserved to have had my life ended at the stake, wouldn't I?"

"Well, you would because to the Inquisition your philosophy is as simple as it is dangerous."

"I'm a sinner who fancies the earth to be an orange he's holding in his hands and who enjoys life, as happy as a child, for as long as God still suffers him to walk the earth."

"I see that to you, Galileo, God and happiness may be pretty much referred to in the same words."

"Because God and happiness are alike. You seek Him even though you will never meet Him."

"You're playing with words, Galileo."

"Not in the least. You may find my words immoderate perhaps because you're too young to understand what lies within an old man's heart. But you will learn some day that only the old can give each day its due. When I was young, I used to live life on the run and never took the time to think that when all is said and done, a love could be tragic because you can see its end. Unfortunately, at my age almost everything has melted into memories. And all the time, I can't help comparing 'what I have now' to 'what I had then'."

"Why did you stop talking?"

"Because I was about to say something silly. That I would like to pass away in the summertime so I can have before my eyes that which I will lose. But death is ugly in any season, while life is beautiful in ways one least expects. I was convinced of this once more before I recanted."

"Convinced how?"

"While watching the smoke from the candles trailing up the walls, I heard a dog barking. At that moment, that bark gained all my attention. It was all that could get through from the world outside. I felt a lump in my throat, but I didn't want to let my uneasiness show. I was afraid that I would offend them or plant suspicions in their heads. You have to trust me when I say that the only thing we love with every fibre of our bodies is that which we might lose. And no one will ever persuade me that death is all sweetness and light."

"Did not Giordano Bruno love life? If what they say about his relationships with women was true, then he must have loved life as few others had ever done."

"I don't know what he felt. All I do know is what I feel on summer days, here . . . . If only I were younger, I'd be galloping round these hills like a wild horse. But since I'm not, I content myself with watching the cypresses give up their disconsolate look once the clouds scatter away. Few have understood that this was the truth I had to defend 'there'."

"The Inquisition couldn't care less about such truth."

"You're wrong. The Inquisition wants to intimidate us precisely because it can sense in our love of life a threat to its omnipotence."

"Before he was put on the stake, Giordano Bruno had his tongue tied to keep him from cursing. You, on the other hand, were allowed to speak."

"It was they who decided what I was to say in the long run, but my heart felt different."

"And haven't you really regretted it? Ever?"

"That I walked out alive? Never."

VI

"Yet my subconscious won't stop swarming. My sleep is all a fret and my dreams are invaded by countless oddities, muddy seas, dogs with human eyes, strange things which, had anyone told me about, I would have dismissed as sheer absurdity. One night my room was full of broken hourglasses whose sand kept dripping out. As time went by, I could feel the sand piling up around me. I panicked and wanted to get out, but the wind outside was howling like a she-wolf raging mad at the loss of her cubs. Eventually, I felt relieved when I saw Ana, and I tried to get closer to her, convinced that only such closeness could keep me safe. *Don't touch me*, she said under her breath. Her barely discernible explanation baffled me. *If you touch my hair or my shoulders now*, she said, *I'll fade away and many hundreds of years will have to pass until I can be born again from the desert. Stay where you are and try to keep calm. Avoid saying my name or calling me.* Afterwards she sank into silence as if she was tired of speaking. I remained still until Ana turned around and opened the door to leave. Right then my panic returned, and I followed her through the sand. When I reached the wall next to the door, I realized that it was completely cold, quite frozen. Besides, it was giving off a sweetish, sickening odour which felt familiar somehow. I could not hold out any longer, and I called out her name: Ana. She stopped and eyed me reproachfully

41

suggesting that had I called her name earlier, my lack of caution might have proven fatal to her. I whispered to her: If all becomes dead time, then the snakes will be just sand snakes, too. They won't be able to bite me. Whenever I feel them crawling up my body again, all I'll need to do is shake off the sand . . . . I had to wait for the wind to die down to hear her answer: *The snakes are real, Galileo. . . .*"

VII

"Let's go back to the moment you recanted."

"The recantation was a mere formality. I hoped that everyone would understand that. To keep my life, I formally recanted a truth which, in any case, no one can ever alter. Whether I had recanted it or not, the earth wouldn't have stopped spinning. It would have kept going round and round, and I, the inquisitors on their thrones, the ones waiting to see whether they needed to carry firewood to the public square to erect a stake and those getting themselves ready to attend the performance – we all would have spun along with it. The earth would have not ceased spinning. Not even for a second."

"*Eppur si muove,* as you muttered on your way out. "

"Precisely. And I was taken aback to find out afterwards that what I was reproached with was a formality. The disavowal was only on my lips. Deep down inside, I've never retracted my belief."

"Do you honestly think that the inquisitors didn't know it was a mere formality? Do you really think them such fools to imagine that they wouldn't realise you'd stick to your views? They never doubted that. No, what they were really interested in was not your ideas. They wanted to put on a show, to arrange, as you yourself called it, a mere 'formality', to give you the official and public opportunity to disavow your beliefs so that others wouldn't be tempted to follow you. This is what they wanted: to disgrace you, not to educate you."

"I am still faithful to my beliefs."

"Galileo, the goal of any inquisition is to create two realities. One seen, the other unseen. The control over visible reality offers the Inquisition control over invisible reality as well. Thus, people get used to believing that it doesn't matter what one thinks. What matters is what one says. So, everyone says what they are required to say and what they believe they have to say if they want to save their skin. And if at first, they are disgusted with it, afterwards it becomes a habit. Then, many are driven into it by interest. The outcome? I believe you know it. You've seen it. Little by little we all realise that everyone around is lying and pretending and not taking any chances. And so, we wonder: why should I act differently? The very idea of conducting oneself with honesty in a world where hypocrisy alone pays off has come to sound quite insane, a veritable folly."

"Don't you think it's natural for people to defend themselves? After all, we were not all of us born to be martyrs."

"True enough. Nevertheless, you have to admit that the omnipotence of the Inquisition doesn't rely on fear alone. It also counts on the zeal of the frightened to appear harmless. Terror-stricken, we rush to the inquisitors to vouchsafe that indeed we think as they want us to think, that they have no reason at all to suspect us or summon us for interrogation. And your argument that the recantation was a mere formality is, I regret to say, a lame excuse. It was never the Inquisition's goal to get you to change your views. All it wanted was the public proof that not even you had the courage to say what you believed in. And when it happened, many people must have thought to themselves that there was no hope left at all: 'If Galileo himself didn't dare, despite his irrefutable proof that the earth is spinning, how could we?' So, you see, your recantation reduced many people to silence. And there's another thing, Galileo."

"Wouldn't you rather watch summer burn its incense? It is as persuasive as it is free of pathos."

"All right then, as you wish. But one of these days I'm going to see this logic through. That is, of course, unless you'd rather run away from whatever it is you don't want to hear."

"I would not. And what better proof than our conversation? Either way, I wouldn't give up my fair share of the 'possible' that surrounds us, no matter how old I may be. The grass is scented and warm, the gardens are overflowing with flowers, and the olive trees – see? – they turn white when evening is at hand. One can be witness to no higher beauty than the light bathing these astonished cypresses. The excitement I feel in their presence does not coerce me into anything."

"But this is not enough for happiness, Galileo."

"It is enough for me. For now, at least. It is as if the dust I've been raising with my sandals were full of seeds. When the wind scatters it away, it makes the glory of summer even more magnificent. The worst thing you can place within this landscape is a cold heart. Don't you agree? All other words seem useless to me."

"The autumn rains will wash all this away into a memory."

"Everything turns into memories, sooner or later. Why wouldn't I choose what I have now?"

"There are no humans in your happiness, Galileo."

"You're wrong. . . ."

VIII

"Last night, one of Nero's praetorian guards kept asking me again and again: 'Is it so very wretched a thing, this dying?' I kept trying to convince him that this was a line from Vergil which a retainer had recited in reply to Nero's request that he accompany him in his flight after being overthrown. 'I know that', he snapped at me, 'but that's the way it should be. Whatever the gods have done cannot be undone.' And then he grumbled something, his back to me: 'This fellow is scared of a spark after having set the whole sky on fire' . . . . Later on I stayed awake till dawn, thinking that the only human thing about Nero had been his end: that he had not had the heart to drink the poison he had procured; that he had changed his mind after having decided to plunge into the Tiber; that he had wavered over thrusting the dagger into his chest once he could feel its edge; it was only the sound of horses' hooves at the gate that had brought his shaking hand to cut open the carotid with a sigh: 'Oh, what an artist dies in me!' . . . . This is what the summers have truly taught me. That the fear of death, happiness, and love are natural things. And all you have to do is see things naturally, beyond the distortion which the Inquisition forces upon the world, so that you can pity those incapable of feeling such a fear."

"Do you really think this is enough to fight that which kills us? You of all people should know better. You were there and you were forced to recant something about which you had no doubts."

"These are things from a past long gone."

"Even so, they're still haunting you. And your history is no longer your own."

<h2 style="text-align:center">IX</h2>

"If the Inquisition hadn't forced me to recant, none of this would have happened. No one would have blamed me for my joy of life."

"Most certainly not."

"And no one would have seen it as a sign of weakness. Other people are free to profess in all their vainglory the same love of life of which I am expected to be ashamed. Whatever sounds beautiful on their tongue becomes nothing but a justification on mine. But why should I justify myself because I love life like any normal human being?"

"You're too alone to be without fault, Galileo."

"You might want to say that perhaps I am too old to understand why a stake is more persuasive than anything I can say."

"You are all alone, you and your morals based exclusively on the love of life."

"The world will never be devoid of meaning as long as we acknowledge that it sprang out of love. All that lives and all that hums on this earth sprang out of love. Is this not enough to render everything meaningful?"

"In the days when Rome used to put up grandiose welcomes and the people cheered the triumphant general, the soldiers, on the contrary, would hurl abuse at him lest his pride should get the better of him. They would shout at Caesar: 'Ladies are not for the likes of you, you, pumpkin-head, content yourself with whores!' You are forcing me to remind you that your nights are haunted by the kind of dreams from which love is usually excluded."

"Because nearly all I ever dream of is not in its normal shape. Last night I dreamt of a monster. It was a bird-headed monster with bulging frog eyes. And when it opened its mouth it hissed like a snake. It sometimes gave out an insolent laugh just like a whore's. *Recant the thought of my being a monster*, he hissed. And then he laughed again. *Recant and proclaim my beauty*. Then his head started spinning as if it were a whirligig. *Is this how the earth is spinning, Galileo? Take a really good look and then go tell everyone that my neck is so stiff that only an imbecile could believe my head is spinning.* Its last words were drowned in spit and indecent gales of laughter . . . ."

"Don't you find it abhorrent that you have to start all over again, every single night?"

"At the Inquisition, after countless hours of torment, I felt sleepy. I wanted to be left alone, to sleep."

"The snakes hadn't crawled into your dreams yet then. The Inquisition has changed your life."

"There was indeed a time when I would laugh or cry and not remember anything. Now, every sand martin's scream over these hills makes me quiver into remembering Marcus Aurelius' advice: 'Live every day of your life as if it were your last.' There is this dialogue I used to picture quite often: 'I will fulfil your last wish, convict. What is it you wish for?' 'To live'."

"Well, you don't seem to fear that this light will carry you further away from the truth if you linger all alone there for too long."

"Death is the only surprise that might come upon me now. Apart from it, I think I've tried almost everything."

"You're tired now. When you've had your rest, you may wish to reconsider that."

"I doubt it."

X

"There's no doubt, Galileo, that you do love the things you touch. And yet I can't help noticing that there's some bitterness behind your words."

"Have you never sat in the sun and found yourself under a shadow? You remember everything and everything is so alive inside you that you are afraid to make the slightest movement for fear of ruining that moment when you could actually be the one who you've remembered you are."

"You know as well as I do that this is not what life really is."

"But what I feel when I sit on these rocks with the heat of the sun on my cheek, may look equally like happiness or despair precisely because the experiences I have lived through have taught me, nay, forced me to simplify things. I've never before had the time to enjoy my life because of my vanities and my ambitions."

"I cannot argue against it, Galileo, you are alive. No doubt about it. Nevertheless, the Inquisition knew very well what it was doing when they forced you to say what they wanted you to say . . . . Whoever recants always ends up losing all sense of self-worth."

"You're wrong. That was why I avoided telling them anything about myself. And anyway, was there anything I could have revealed which would not have shortened my path to the stake? They will never accept that it is a human heart that lies in the centre of the universe. Perhaps I should have told them: Gentlemen, given that life is the only real philosophical question, I hereby agree to recant my views on the solar system. But this shall be the one and only reason why I'd agree to do it. I, therefore, kindly ask you to lend my gesture its rightful weight and not allow it to suffer any distortions because it is the outcome of certain convictions which run far deeper than those I've agreed to recant, and under no circumstances should it testify to your rightfulness. It is a matter of choice, that's all. My rejection of the stake is also a rejection of that which defines you. So, I'll accept none of your arsenal but the disgrace which will be heaped upon my head for having recanted."

"To tell you the truth, what I find quite intriguing about you, Galileo, is how you obstinately keep coming back to the same episodes."

"Then I will tell you that one is truly free only when nothing can be changed anymore. Only then one feels perfectly round, like a fruit."

"What about when the night comes?"

XI

"Ana spoke to me about Alexander. Whenever she starts speaking of him, the timbre of her voice changes. It grows warm all of a sudden; it becomes soothing and sad as if concealing a mystery. She took me to the middle of a rocky plateau covered with some red shrubbery stunted by the heat of the sun, and with a stick she drew for me the tent in front of which, she said, the young king would stand for hours gazing at the sky on the eve of each of his battles. *He always avoided fighting whenever the sun was burning hot because he never wanted to conquer the world as a human, but as a god*, she whispered to me in explanation. *He had fought his battles to get that which the Greek had denied him by acknowledging his glory as a victor of the world, but unwilling to acknowledge his victory over a bloodless peace.* I noticed a venomous flower blooming on the red shrubs, one that bit you when you tried to smell its perfume. She bent over to pick one of them, and I shouted at her not to touch it. She turned to me and said: *Many of your loved ones are now wandering into the realm of the shadows. Why fear it then?* 'There's only one easy answer to this question,' I told her. 'Because even the dead I cannot love unless I am alive' . . . Then it suddenly started to rain. We found shelter under a rock and watched the thunderbolts gliding into the grass. Ana kept silent for a while. Then, still with her back to me, lingering on her words and gazing at the forked thunderbolts, she said something puzzling: *Right here, under this rock, the only risk you take is that of a slow and peaceful death. The rock will absorb you slowly without making any threats.'* I cannot remember what happened afterwards . . . .

"You too avoid fighting in the blazing sun."

. . . *Oh, yes, I remember. I had this awful dream in which I was a child and I would play in the ashes left from the stakes, but never knew why people were burnt. I would draw animals, trees, and flowers in them. Then I started gathering the ashes to make ash dolls, and when it rained I had to cover them. Some other children watched me doing this and they liked my dolls. They asked me how I had managed to shape them and they began making dolls, too. In the end, so many children gathered round that there were no ashes*

51

left. And so, we all went to find the street where the palace of the Inquisition stood. We waited there for someone to be put on trial. In the evening a woman was taken out, her clothes torn to pieces and her hands tied up with a rope behind her back. We thanked the inquisitors, and they gave us their blessing and encouraged us to make happy dolls.

XII

"Galileo, I must confess that I didn't expect to meet a man haunted by such melancholies and obsessions, prone to seeing life through the eyes of a weary poet. I pictured you in a whole different light, based on the stories chance brought my way."

"What stories?"

"I would rather not upset you."

"There's hardly anything that can upset me these days because there isn't much left that can surprise me."

"Have you really mastered all vanities, you, who are so vain yourself?"

"It seems I've drifted away not only from all others, but also from the man I used to be."

"Is that really so?"

"If you think it all came down to fear, you're mistaken."

"I've come all the way out here because I'm willing to understand. If I wasn't, I would have settled for the stories going around."

"The truth is that what happened there unsettled something deep inside me. One can get over one's fear; other things are not so easy to put behind. It suddenly struck me then that the life I had led was a pretence."

"I should be the one saying this. And once I reveal to you why I was so intent on meeting you, you'll see that this is not in jest. But you had your share of glory, Galileo. The Pope himself showed you his appreciation, and up to a point, he even rose in your defence even though you were far from courteous to him. You wrote books, you are widely read, people are talking about you, you have followers and you have foes. You are envied, pitied . . . . "

" . . . cursed . . . "

"Even curses are a form of recognition after all. You are alive, Galileo, unlike me, a ghost. But you're the one acting like a ghost."

"And how exactly did you expect me to be? Happy? Well, you should know then that I'm nearly blind. With each day that passes, my sight grows weaker and weaker. Perhaps this will help you understand why I keep talking about the summer light. I feel forced to look inside myself more and more often, and when the day comes that complete darkness finally descends upon me, this will be all that I'll have left."

"It's true that I have heard talk of your afflicted eyesight, but I never suspected it to be of such severity."

"I'm glad I can still hear at least. Late at night, when tormented by my insomnia, I needed to listen to some music, and I feared I would lose my hearing, too. But you still haven't answered my question: How did you expect me to be?"

"I don't know if the unvarnished truth will do any good."

"Rest assured that nothing can really hurt me now. Do tell, I'm listening."

"The rumour has it that your sharp tongue had earned you lots of enemies and that you would tolerate neither being ignored nor contradicted. Your mind was – or at least this is what the gossipmongers say – far more brilliant than your nature. Whoever dared disagree with you soon after found they'd been labelled as a nitwit. You jeered at philosophers by saying they'd fallen asleep in Aristotle's arms, and yet you didn't hesitate to fawn on your benefactors to serve your needs. The Jesuits were not particularly demanding. They would have suffered you to assert your ideas if only you had done it with less clamour and defiance and not placed the Pope himself into such an awkward position. You fancied that no one would have the courage to pick on you. You backed down only when fear conquered you. They say your bravery lasted only until the moment of your arrest."

"It was spring, I remember. The 12th day of April . . . ."

"Did they torture you?"

"No, they didn't. But the threat of torture is torture enough . . . . After I recanted, I had to do daily penance by reciting seven psalms under surveillance. I wasn't allowed to go out, and few people were given permission to visit me. Now at least they let me stroll along these hills and feast my poor old eyes on the summer view before complete blindness sets in."

"Have you ever renounced God, if even for a moment?"

"No, I haven't. How could I do a thing like that? All I did was to say that God has His reasons which human reason knows not. Even though I might have regarded the heavens more frostily than I should have done, I have never permitted myself, even for a moment, to ravage them. I believe in divine mystery, even though I'm quite incapable, as you can see, of telling apart the sacred from the profane pleasures. Do you find my words puzzling?"

"No, Galileo, I don't."

XIII

"You realize then that I'm more justified than others to loathe the inquisitors. But I've never thought that loathing them as a victim, on the stake, can be of much use. And unfortunately, flames are the only thing people remember."

"Because their price has always been a human life."

"Don't you think that the humiliation I was put through deserves some consideration? And it's not respect I'm asking for, just some consideration. It wasn't easy for me at all, you know. And don't you find it immoral that people who have never had to squeak by the stake, who have never been dragged, as I have,

55

before the court of the Inquisition, who have never been interrogated or threatened, should put me on trial for my fear?"

"'Fear', said Leonardo, 'travels faster and arrives sooner.'"

"Not to mention that it is not those who have to endure the fear who are the problem, but the ones who beget it. There is a cause for every fear. This is what people forget. Instead, they never stop talking about my recantation. As if this were what was shameful: me and my stubborn will to live, not those who reduced me to fear. Now, you tell me how fair this is."

"But it is our fear that makes terror what it is, don't you agree, Galileo? The inquisitors wanted to get hold of our souls, and they succeeded."

"When they threatened to torture me, one of the inquisitors couldn't keep his eyes off my fingers. As if he felt sorry that I was going to get away too lightly."

"When I listen to you, Galileo, I feel both a sense of brotherhood and a sort of unease. Both of these feelings I'll explain to you later. But you have to agree that no other torture instrument is as necessary to the Inquisition as fear. Besides, its work is hygienic, no blood, no screams. It operates discreetly. And truth to tell, the Inquisition is not just an institution. Or it is rather more than an institution. It is like a disease, like a plague paralyzing the honesty in humans. It dwells in each and every one of us."

"Your words hold an uncanny truth."

"We're all of us, or nearly all of us, in the service of the Inquisition through our fears, even though we don't find any pleasure in admitting it. By allowing ourselves to be scared we have encouraged it to grow even bolder."

"But how can you master your fear? Can anyone ever do that?"

"Some people could, Galileo. I feel bound to remind you of it once again."

"But what was the price they paid? Accepting the stake is not an answer."

"Are you going to be preaching again that life is worth much more than ideas?"

"I'm not preaching anything. I merely wish to explain to you how I feel. That's all. And to tell you that it is a poorly made and twisted world that we live in if we have to burn in flames to prove our beliefs. I think the stakes are a folly. A mockery and . . . yes, a folly."

"And does it not surprise you that people judge you?"

"No, not anymore. I've realized that it requires no great effort for people to set themselves up as judges of others' misfortunes."

"Galileo, you remind me of a sick man who refuses to talk about his illness, telling himself that this is his way of defending himself against it."

"I fight only those things which deny and offend me. "

XIV

"Love alone could never extinguish the stakes, Galileo."

"Each night I need courage . . . to go to bed."

"Another nightmare, I gather?"

"It was as though someone had cursed the inquisitors to listen, night after night, to a lesson on the rotation of the earth. This was happening actually, after we, the inquisitors and I, had both passed away, and so the threat to be burnt at the stake was nothing more than a memory. Suddenly, one of them broke out: 'It's useless, Galileo! The verdict delivered during your lifetime remains final!' A gale of laughter filled the place. I understood then that it was futile and I looked down. I wanted to kill myself, but I was already dead."

"What they couldn't forgive you is your will to live beyond their dogmas."

"I wanted to live according to my mind."

"You still need to find out that wisdom begins where all ambiguity ends."

"And what's ambiguous about my words?"

"There is sadness and there is brightness in your words."

"I've never wished to be a sage."

"You force me to tell you, Galileo, that you do not love the truth the same way you do a serene sky."

"Had I finally had the power to sentence the inquisitors, I would have sentenced them to love the world. I'm convinced this would have been the worst punishment for them. I know these things well . . . ."

XV

"It looks as though nothing else interests you anymore, except for your feelings. You're thinking with your heart now, Galileo."

"Perhaps reason gets tired before the heart does. And I can't even tell whether this is good or not."

"Why do you doubt?"

"When you feel more than you can understand, you become vulnerable. The inquisitors are that self-assured because they lack feelings. They can even hate whatever they cannot understand whereas someone like me gets caught up in his own regrets."

"Did you say you have feelings you don't understand?"

"Let me give you an example. I was wandering in a forest covered in darkness, and when I had nearly lost all hope of ever finding my way out of it, I saw through the pine trees – for it was a pine forest – a light flickering in the dark. I headed for it, and as I got closer, the light grew brighter and brighter. But emerging from behind a mound, I came upon something which stunned me. The light was coming from a huge fire. Frightened, I rushed back but then I heard a jeering voice telling me that running away was pointless because there was no other way out of the forest. And so I turned round and headed towards the fire. 'What will be, will be', I told myself. *It's no use, Galileo*, the voice told me. *You have to lose all hope first. Only then will the stake become a mere formality.* 'And how long do I have to wander like that?' I shouted. *That depends on you, Galileo*, the voice answered. *No one can help you if your heart remains stubbornly hopeful. It is only when nothing stirs your interest anymore that you'll be ready for the stake....*"

"And what's so confusing about this?"

"What courage is that which makes you accept death when you no longer have the will to live? Sometimes I walk to the edge of the pine forest nearby and I wait. When the days are peaceful, there's the sound of a spring that I hear which cleanses my soul and leaves only pure joy within. In moments like this, it occurs to me that this is what the secret heart of life must look like. In the evening, I count the stars lighting up in the sky. Just as if I were counting seashells on a beach, my fingers all wet and full of sand. I don't notice how tired or old I am anymore. And everything happens naturally; there are no constraints. It's a silence which depends on me alone and one I wish could last forever."

"You couldn't live like this forever."

"I know that. And yet, I'm grateful to every hour which doesn't remind me that I couldn't."

"There, at the edge of that pine forest, lies only half of what you are. It is your selfish half, the one which refuses to know anything about anyone else, all in the name of the idea that happiness is a strictly private matter. But you have another half, too, Galileo, the one which — if it's true what the legend says — whispered *eppur si muove* and thus bound itself to abiding by what is obvious. You do not have the right to not know that there are victims, no matter how glad you may be to have walked free."

"Those who are truly brave avoid talking about courage."

"And how long would a silence which relies only on such avoidance last? A moment, an hour, a night? What we must wish for, Galileo, is a silence with its eyes wide open."

"I hardly think that possible."

"Why not?"

"That's how I feel. I'd find it difficult to explain why. It might have been easier to agree with you before."

"Now you're rubbing salt in your wounds."

"Perhaps I am. People like me are never tired of mulling things over and over."

"It seems that sometimes you wish to be like Ana."

"One night she confessed to me that she too needed to forget. 'What is it you want to forget?' I asked her. At first, she went silent and so I stopped asking. Then she spoke, but she was so far away from me that I could barely hear what she said: *Each of us has something to forget* . . . . Her voice was like a slightly discernible tremor which I mistook for the rustle of the cypresses: *Why would I tell you something you wouldn't believe anyway?* Her voice died away, and all I could hear in the end were indeed the cypresses soughing in the wind."

XVI

"It seems to me you don't like calling all things by their names."

"Does the heart really need words? The brain cannot do without them, but when it comes to feelings, you can just feel without the need to distinguish between one tree and the other or even between a tree and a man. All you have to do is feel the bark of the pines with your fingers, watch their branches and listen to their rustle. I happened to try such a soul therapy myself. And I can assure you that I found it most useful. I don't know whether I could have survived without it . . . . All my life I was so confident. It turns out that I was just very skilled at noticing only the bright side of doubts. And then, suddenly, I saw only their dark side. Everything had shattered, I had lost all my confidence, and I didn't know what I could or could not rely on anymore. The humiliations I had to endure at the Inquisition had dried up my soul. My self-confidence which had always given me such a sense of pride – almost conceit you might say – gave way and threatened to turn me into nothing more than a rotten pole left by the side of the road. And so, to keep myself from falling, I decided to follow my heart instead of my mind. This way, I could afford to have feelings without having to understand them. Because I was beyond understanding. I had had too many unpleasant revelations in a very short period of time, and I'd never shown much promise as a stoic. What's more, I have to admit that were I to brush some of the exaggerations aside, the portrait of me you painted, based on what you'd heard, is real. Or rather was real. I could never stand being contradicted, and I helped my enemies multiply rapidly. I overestimated both my capabilities and the patience of the Inquisition. I placed too much faith on my lucky star and my fame. And I might have trusted people far too much. Be that as it may, I misjudged the situation. In my polemic with the Jesuits, which was quite lengthy, I was the one adding fuel to the fire. I hadn't really thought about what would come of it. Perhaps I was a poor player after all and never realized it, goaded as I was by vanity into not letting things go. I should have known that they wouldn't suffer such boldness. In a way, you could say that I asked for trouble. That was what it took for me to be rid of all conceit. It is true, however, that I was fed up with their whims and that it was more and more difficult for me to pretend. And a thing like this is very dangerous in a society gripped by the fear of the Inquisition. As long as you pretend, the Inquisition will leave you alone. They don't care about what you believe in. All that counts is not to talk, not to give yourself away. Honesty, now this is what they cannot stand. That is why, as soon as they notice that you've crossed a line beyond which they no longer put up with your views, they'll declare you a heretic. And that very moment the war has already begun. You have only two choices left then: penance or the stake . . . . After my recantation, the woman guarding me would watch closely to be sure I'd recited my seven daily psalms. I wasn't allowed to go out for walks. I was terribly downhearted. To top it all, I realized that my eyesight was getting worse. I was afraid I might go blind before I could see the dear places of my youth one more time, and I resolved to take a stand before it was too late. I started shouting that I couldn't stand being locked up anymore, that I would choke. The woman guarding me got frightened and went to inform them. The outcome was that they let me come here. They must have thought: What's the harm? He is free to talk to the cypresses as much as he wishes and to explain to them this whole earth rotation business. What matters is that he is not surrounded by people. They didn't suspect that I might meet someone here. In fact, I'm quite surprised that there's been no one to spy on us yet . . . . This crisis drained me of all the energy I had left, it simply wore me out. It even left a bad taste in my mouth . . . . As a matter of fact, what I want you to remember is that it wasn't easy for me to subject myself to such merciless self-searching – I, who was used to going easy on myself, being so content with who I was, not setting much store by things unless they interested me."

"But what if I'm one of the Inquisition spies, Galileo? What if I was sent out here purposely to pump you for your secrets, to find out what you're hiding?"

"Well, the idea never occurred to me, I'll admit."

"And aren't you afraid of such a possibility, you who are so prudent?"

"Well, what could you possibly tell them they don't know already? That I love life? That I hate the stake? That I'm old and nearly blind? Neither my sickness nor fear of them is any secret. The only news you could bring them is that I have nightmares every single night."

"There's nothing for you to be worried about, Galileo. I was indeed acquainted with the Inquisition, but I have no reasons to serve it. Quite the opposite."

"You do act mysteriously."

"All in good time, Galileo. But in the meantime, let me tell you that your love of life nurtures no certainties. And you don't have to be as cruel as they are to be like them. Keeping your mind on the cypresses alone is quite enough."

"Trust me, I'm sick and tired of keeping my mind on nothing but the foul and the ugly. This world has beauty to offer, too. What a pity that I won't live to see it for many summers to come . . . . You should try looking at things the way I do."

"I'd be afraid of doing that, Galileo, because this is not why I've come here. And I wouldn't want you to have any illusions about it."

"The day I can bring myself to remember everything and be resigned to it, that day I might refrain from defending myself. But I haven't reached that point yet. I still carry the conviction that my heart is right. And in any event, if I am to be a 'victim', it seems that it's my destiny to be a discreet victim. The only worry I have is that my nights haven't found their peace yet."

XVII

"The day will come when the earth will spin carrying with it not only our graves but the graves of those we are frightened of. But it's what people will remember that matters."

"And what do you think they will remember about me?"

"That you recanted, of course. That you recanted a truth."

"Is there a higher truth than life itself?"

"I take it you would have made a good sophist."

"I wish people would remember the real reason I was arrested by the inquisitors and forced to recant. They knew what I meant by claiming that the earth was turning. They realized that what I was actually doing was calling into question their entire world order."

"But they realized something else too. That fear will make you soft."

"Last night I was thinking that on a clear day, the sunset is beautiful even over a blood-soaked battlefield. Don't I have the right to watch the sunset over such a field but perhaps without the blood?"

"It is a somewhat sad right, Galileo. Unless you join the killed, you will be taking the side of the killer."

"Sometimes I feel that the only difference between Nero and destiny might be just in the terminology . . . why are you smiling?"

"You've mentioned Nero twice already."

"And why does that come as a surprise to you?"

"I thought you'd be telling me about the Jesuits, not about a madman from ancient Rome."

"This madman is the model for the advocates of the wisdom of fear. Shall I surprise you further? I would find it difficult to explain why, but the obscure side of ancient Rome's history has always been of interest to me. It beggars belief what befell the Roman emperors who succeeded Marcus Aurelius . . . Commodus, who was in the habit of stabbing a tiger every morning, was found strangled in his bathroom by his praetorian guard. His successor too was found murdered two months later. Caracalla was stabbed. Heliogabalus, murdered at his grandmother's order. Severus Alexander, killed in his tent. Maximinus, who was six and a half feet tall and had fingers so thick that he wore his wife's bracelets as rings, was assassinated by soldiers; Gordian shared the same fate; Philip the Arab had his head split open; Decius, killed by the Goths; Gallus, assassinated by the soldiers who hailed Emilianus, only to kill him as well two months later. Galienus had the same fate. Aurelian, assassinated; Probus, murdered as well. Until Diocletian, the throne of Rome was a slaughterhouse block. In an entire century of murders and killings, the only one to have died in his own bed was Tacitus, one of the historian's descendants, but then he died a few months after his ascension to the throne as he was very old . . . ."

"Sometimes history can teach you how easy it is to die."

"I doubt this is something that needs teaching. Not that it was news to me, but I was shocked to find out that the inquisitors could kill with God's name on their lips."

"You see – how can I put this? God can have no better face than what we are capable of giving Him. The one who sets stakes ablaze whilst calling God's name will always turn Him into a bloodthirsty idea . . . . Isn't it strange, Galileo, that the absence of ideas has claimed less blood than their presence?"

"When they became one with the prisons. And the stakes. But what's the good of a faith if what lies at the end of it is crime? If an idea needs the stakes to exalt it, then it's an idea not worth living."

"The Inquisition begs to differ. It did away with the difference between prayer and murder…. Before the Inquisition, you could hate as if you were praying."

"Then you understand why I was afraid of them."

"I understand it quite well, but fear cannot work as an excuse for everything."

"It sounds so simple when you say it! I wish I could have seen your bravery when you faced that look in their eyes. "

"I did, but not in court, it is true."

"Where, then?"

"I'm someone of no importance. You are Galileo Galilei."

"The inquisitors wouldn't have shied away from making an example out of me to show all dissenters what awaits the heretic."

"This way they can set an example of submission. They make a show of it, one in which you can be seen on your knees. Once the others have seen it, no one would dare deny the omnipotence of the Inquisition."

"But I'm not at all interested in being made into an example. There's something else that I wish for, if only it were possible."

"For the courts not to exist anymore?"

"I don't aim that high. I would settle for good sight, not to have to bend over all the time so I can hear what you're saying. For this, I would recant anything. Unfortunately, it's impossible."

"Some say you think little of martyrs, that you consider them fanatics."

"But perhaps I am a fanatic myself, in my own way. No one has ever been able to talk me out of the belief that I have no other life but this one, so that I end up despising what I defended . . . . And why is it that some people are always comparing me to the martyrs? I don't see them doing the same for those who forced the martyrs into sacrifice. Does not one of the Ten Commandments say 'Thou shalt not kill'?"

"All the Inquisition wanted was for you to act selfishly and then start looking for consolation. They planned this right."

"That I find the summer exquisitely beautiful shouldn't bother anyone."

"But this is not about the beauty of summer, Galileo."

"Yes, it is. Don't you see how we keep coming back to the same point?"

"What do you think a heretic is?"

"A lonely man . . . Someone like me . . . A man who must be uprooted from society or forced to live his life amongst the cypresses because he uses his mind to come up with ideas of his own which differ from the mandatory ones. And this is something the Inquisition cannot tolerate."

"If it did, it would be signing its own death sentence . . . ."

"You were surprised to see how much I cherish my vital instinct. Well, if I'm wrong, it would be the Inquisition's fault because it swapped places with death and made me realise that now I do love life, but not happily, as I used to do in my days of youth. No, now it's with despair."

"You're an odd man, Galileo."

"Why?"

"Your prudence made you fear everything except people's prejudice. Considered that way, you almost have the soul of a child . . . ."

XVIII

"But this doesn't help me silence some of the doubts I have."

"About me?"

"No, not about you, Galileo. With your help, what I'm trying to do is judge myself. As a matter of fact, I wonder whether it is enough not to become a victim."

"The Inquisition might yet have a philosophical mission into the world, for all we know."

"Are you being ironic?"

"Not entirely . . . but the question remains whether you have to go to hell to genuinely appreciate its opposite."

"That is, whether we can know happiness without ever knowing pain – is that what you mean?"

"The dream I had last night and especially the conclusion of it, made me think . . . . I was lying down, somewhere in the snow, in the woods, my left foot broken against a frozen pine tree which the wind had thrown to the ground. I was crying for help when suddenly I heard the wolves howling. The noise was so terrifying, it made the entire woods shudder. The howling stopped only when I started shouting. The wolves were listening, using my cries to work out how to find me. As I kept crying, they got closer, guided by my voice. How about that? To cry for help and summon the wolves, that's quite something, isn't it?"

"Well, it's rather sad."

"I had but one solution left to defend myself: to dig my nails into my flesh and keep quiet."

"Speaking of which, there are so many things which are not easy to talk about . . . ."

"The Inquisition being one of them, too."

"I agree, Galileo. Were it not . . . . "

"Were it not?"

"I would have told you a few things from the start . . . but carry on."

"I had known fame, had friends in high places. I cannot complain that I didn't enjoy the privileges life offered me. Fate was kind to me. But, despite all that, now when I'm almost blind and broken . . . because humiliation too is a stake . . . now I can see more clearly the truths I used to overlook. My life, such as it has been these past few years, has forced this lesson upon me: that it is precisely that which threatens us that gives us our depth. Never have I loved the earth more than after the Inquisition asked for my opinion about it."

"So it turns out that Empedocles was not naive. There's only love and strife."

"The Inquisition made me feel things I might not have felt otherwise. The discovery of fear taught me to love passionately all I was in danger of losing. They talked to me about God and so it was that I discovered how intimately close I felt to what is human. And is there anything more human than to feel vulnerable?"

"Even your bitterness is sunlit."

"When I was living my life buried under a pile of books, I rarely indulged in the luxury of lying idly in the warm grass, the least expensive of luxuries and yet the one closest to the mystery of life. One day I went to the seashore and there I saw a diver looking for seashells. He would plunge into the waves, and on coming up, he would open his fist to check what he had managed to pick up. Sometimes, there was nothing there, only sand. Other times, there were wet seashells shimmering in the sand. But each and every time it was only when he was above the water, out in the daylight that he could appreciate what he held in his fist . . . ."

"It's obvious that by humiliating you, the Inquisition stirred up a vanity of a different kind inside you."

"I see these hills in a whole different light now, although I had gone rambling in them so many times before. The sun, too, looks different now when it rises above the damp heads of the cypresses."

"Perhaps destiny is only that which we can remember."

XIX

"Ana took me back again in Alexander's footsteps. The grass got thinner and thinner and the cypresses shorter and shorter. The blades of grass let steep rocks peep out from amongst them; then the trees vanished. The sky took on the colour of sand, and I recognized around us the rocky plateau where we had been before; only there was no red shrubbery this time. *You can find your peace here*, said Ana and she stopped walking. *You needn't fear anymore. They'll never find you here.* 'Are you sure?' *And even if they did, there's no wood here to build up a fire. They can threaten you as much as they please. They would never be able to see it through.* The hot sun was glaring above our heads. The rock shone like a mirror, and had you felt it with your fingers, it would have burnt you. Ana spoke again: *You can find your peace here.* I looked around. 'But there's too much loneliness here . . . . This is not what I recanted for . . . .' *Have it your way*, said Ana in a voice in which I could sense neither approval nor reproof. *Have it your way, then . . . . But here you could have left everything behind."*

XX

"Still, you are drowning in loneliness, Galileo."

"I'm just like a bird roused from its sleep, screaming with the sun blinding it as it rises."

"You're pretending not to understand what I mean. You're always hiding behind words, evading whatever you dislike."

"I am not evading anything. You're wrong. I'm just trying to sort out my memories."

"And yet, you keep pitting the present against them."

74

"What else could I pit against them now?"

"The ideas you once believed in. The earth still spins on."

"I'm not that vain, to imagine that there is still someone interested in my beliefs."

"In this light, you face no other threat but loneliness, Galileo."

"Don't you think I know better what threats I am facing? One day the light was streaming down the trees and the air was white, and it made me feel elated, weightless, free from all memories and fears. Somewhere, not far from where I was, I noticed two strangers who lay in the grass, talking. One of them kept fingering a blade of grass. The other one asked him a question I didn't understand. Eventually, the man spoke just when I thought he had lost interest in everything except in his blade of grass: 'Sometimes we fail to cherish the natural things which surround us. Just imagine being doomed to set fire to everything you lay your hands on. Set fire to the water you bring to your lips, the grass you lie on. Only then would you discover the true meaning of loneliness. . . .'"

XXI

"Then I heard a cypress rustling . . . . Two cold hands held my face, and a slightly hoarse voice said softly: *Don't worry, stop thinking about unpleasant things* . . . . 'I will', I said, 'but stay with me, please.' *I'll stay*, Ana whispered. *I'll stay because we share a scar.* I found her words reassuring, even though I didn't know what to make of them. But soon after I was alone again. And I thought that my loneliness must have moulded into my destiny."

"See, you're obsessed with loneliness."

"And what am I supposed to do?"

"Share it with somebody. Share it with people, Galileo, not with the trees, the stones or the sky."

"Right now peace is what I need the most."

"I have the feeling you wish for something more."

"Is there no peace which can be craved for? Even if I am to share it with the trees, the stones and the sky? . . . The trees, the stones and the sky – they have never offended me. Here, in this place, nobody has threatened or forced me into accepting beliefs contrary to what I feel. If I'm thirsty, I bend down and drink water from a spring; if I'm sad, I watch the clouds and the birds. Once I used to wander around these same places, but I never saw what I see now. In those days, a hill was just a hill, a cypress was just a cypress, everything went by its own name. Back then none of these things yet spelt life, love, past, or hope. But now everything I come across speaks to me about what I carry inside. Yet these words are free from all constraint, even when all I am is a man chased by a stake, as Ana used to say. At times I find black traces of fire in the grass. At first I feel sick. Then I tell myself that not all fires are started by the Inquisition and neither do they all force people into abjuration. On these hills, no one asks me to face anything other than the rain, the wind, and my memories. And when my loneliness becomes too heavy to bear, I postpone remembering until later on and try to fall asleep. In the daytime, I have no dreams and I can rest. One day when I opened my eyes I saw a snake in the grass. I shooed it away and that was all there was to it. Here everything is settled naturally; even happiness itself goes by a simple name. Just like time. Or death. And what summer does is to awaken in me all my desires and all my regrets. I'm almost like Oedipus. Pain has taught me to be free."

"I'm afraid I'm going to disappoint you and tell you something utterly unpleasant. Your childlike soul may not forgive my cruelty, but I'm at a loss for a better choice of words than the ones that came to me while listening to you. The stake has accomplished its mission, Galileo, and the Inquisition has attained its goal, if your loneliness indeed resembles the loneliness of the plants."

"I find your words vague."

"What the Inquisition aimed for was not necessarily to have you killed, but to stir up in you a fear that would reduce you in stature to something comparable to a plant. The Inquisition sought to turn you into a plant, Galileo. Ashes leave behind traces and compromise, plants pass unnoticed. And you're not far off from sharing this destiny. The only thing which still holds you back is your memory. What you should pray for is to forget nothing of what happened."

XXII

"So it is all my fault again?"

"Your fault, Galileo, lies in more than just your abjuration."

"What other sins do people charge me with?"

"That you showed no resistance whatsoever to the inquisitors' philosophy. You did not fight their morality by pitting a different one against it."

"But their morality is the stake. I did fight the stake."

"By exculpating yourself."

"And what was I supposed to do?"

"To question the stake as a way of thinking. If Rome was overflowing with corpses during Caligula's reign, it was because it accepted the rationale of murder. How else would it have been possible for an emperor to demand that his senators kiss his feet and have his horse elected as consul? Or close the granaries and decree mandatory famine; or, on a mere whim, just because that day he happened not to like the look of someone's head on their shoulders, to kill . . . How did Rome fight against all these horrors?"

"Caligula was stabbed."

"Murder can never replace a morality meant to actually help one fight other murders."

"I cannot fight murder. I cannot stand the sight of blood."

"But you must face the truth. And its consequences too, Galileo."

"How many times do I have to tell you that I'd sooner stay with those truths which help me live? This way I can feel I've made my peace with the world."

"With the world perhaps, Galileo, but not with those whose way of thinking is murderous."

"No sooner had mankind found God than they had to crucify a man so heaven could be provided with its morality."

"It wasn't heaven I was thinking about, but the anomaly which is the Inquisition and which has to be fought by an opposing idea, a truth, not mere loneliness."

"I cannot believe that all truth teaches us is pain and pain alone. As long as I live and I'm still able to abhor the stakes, I shall be convinced that what I did was right."

"Your life was not the only one at stake there. You shouldn't ignore this."

"But my life was the only one that was threatened: This dream I had is the proof of it: A fellow with a rather oblong head that he kept dangling over the table was shrieking with laughter. *All right, Galileo, recant and you'll be free.* A few moments later, after I had recanted perhaps, I was out in the street. And as I was walking, I bumped into a wall. I followed the length of it until I found myself out of the city and into a wasteland where I lay down to sleep, trying to rid myself of my sickness. When I woke up, the sun was beating down mercilessly and my whole body was burning up like a wound. I stood up and I made for the hills which I could see in the distance ahead, but I ended up running into the same wall. I walked on through the burning sand until my feet were bleeding, watching the adumbral olive trees and cypresses swaying beyond the wall when all of a sudden, I realised that the wall was slowly being erected as I walked, following the direction of my footsteps. Slaves were the ones building it, their bodies bathed in sweat, whipped incessantly by the same inquisitors who had tried me. The oblong-headed fellow shouted at me from across the wall: *Stop running, Galileo. By the time you've reached the end of the wall, it will have gone all the way round the earth. But we'll let you go; you won't be locked up inside it.* And again he shrieked with laughter until I heard his voice once more: *Aren't you curious, Galileo, to know what these slaves are singing while building this wall at your feet*? They were, indeed, singing a sad song which I had taken for the moaning wind. The song was nothing more than a repetition of the same words, sung obsessively in an anguished and flat tone: *The earth does not spin, the earth does not spin* . . . . Soon afterward, they fell silent. *It's done, Galileo*, I heard the inquisitor's sharp voice, *the wall is now complete. From now on, no one will ever disturb you in your wasteland.*"

"So, it appears I was right, the goal of the Inquisition was not necessarily to have you killed, but for you to be left all alone."

XXIII

"Some time later I dreamt of the same inquisitor, in Rome, wearing Nero's toga. He was standing in front of a mirror, talking. At first, I thought he might be talking to someone behind him. Afterwards I realized that there was no one else in the room. He was talking while looking at himself in the mirror and pausing to caress the fur of a huge dog sitting at his feet: *I kill because this is the only thing which makes my life meaningful. It is my destiny to be understood only when my hands are smeared with blood . . . when I appear merciless and very lonely . . . . I can always read the fear and the hatred quivering on the lips of those who talk to me. And when I see it, I can feel an urge to strike rising within me. I try to fill my loneliness with blood and corpses. Yet no one ever suspects how miserable I am . . . . One single genuine love would be enough to save me, perhaps, from all these murders. It could give me what I get from cramming the beasts in the Coliseum . . . . But everywhere I look, all I see are fellows turning pale and ready to recant their beliefs in the most revolting manner no sooner than you mention death to them.* At that very moment, the servants dragged into the room a man in chains, his wrists and ankles swollen and covered in blood. Bored, the emperor turned around and waited. Then he started showing signs of annoyance. *Humiliate yourself but make it quick, I'm in a hurry*, he commanded. The man didn't say anything. *You are sentenced to death*, Nero cried. The chained man still kept his composure. The servants started dragging him to the exit. *Wait*, the emperor commanded. And, in a state of baffled irritation, he asked the victim: *What's your name?* The condemned man burst into laughter. I thought he was mad. But his answer woke me up: *My name is Galileo Galilei.*"

"I imagine you would have loved to have the courage of the man in your dream."

"Do tell me: do you think that all abjuration is unworthy? If something can drive you into hesitation, can it really be that inconsequential?

"I would like to know the answer to this question too, Galileo . . . . But you don't mention Ana anymore."

XXIV

"Every night I can barely wait to hear her husky voice, and every day I grow more convinced that she has a secret to hide."

"Just like you, Galileo."

"Everyone knows my secret."

"Not entirely."

"Instead of dreaming about her, I dreamt about something disgusting. One of the inquisitors said to me: *Come, Galileo, come and see for yourself how your attempts to forget us are pointless.* We walked through the pine forest, headed for the forester's cabin. A suspicion sprang up in my mind. Maybe he was going to let the snakes loose on me . . . . But no, that was not what he had planned. He didn't go to the door but walked around the cabin and stopped by a back window instead, looked inside, and beckoned me to approach. When I put my face against the window, I was dumbfounded. What I saw inside the cabin was myself, watching the snakes licking drops of blood off the floor. *Our only concern*, the inquisitor whispered in explanation, *was to plant some memories of us in you, Galileo. 'We knew that once you had them, you'd never go a day without them.'* I ran away and hid in a pit where no one ever sets foot. I thought that there I could learn to be like a cypress. I stood rooted to the spot, barely breathing. Some time later there were no other sounds but those that could be heard in the forest. It was enough for me then to catch a glimpse of the mountain ridge at the hour when the sun was going down. The crest was ablaze. And although it should have brought thoughts of the approaching night, it was the stakes instead that came to my mind."

XXV

"Your nights are making me increasingly concerned."

"And you think I'm not? But you don't know the whole story yet. I tried to stay as far away as possible from an odd bird laying black eggs which she sat on with great maternal care for a long time, only to kill the chicks with her beak the moment they hatched. Then she would start all over again . . . . Finally, when I could no longer put up with it, I tried to kill her. Instead of flying away, she kept looking at me, waiting. Her cruelty was so full of sorrow that I pitied her and put my hand out to caress her. Only then did she open up her wings and vanish. *Poor bird*, said Ana, *she's in despair because she cannot love her chicks. That's why she kills them. She is mad.'"*

XXVI

"If you want the full picture of what's swarming around in my subconscious, I could go on. . . . It might be sufficient for you to hear that recanting wasn't that easy for me. It was as though I hadn't been released by the Inquisition yet, and I was thrown into a prison cell waiting to be told in the night what verdict they had decided on. I heard footsteps near the door which were to bring me either life or the stake. I was lurking behind the door like a beast; the sound of the footsteps on the stone grew louder and louder, and I couldn't bring myself to imagine the face of the truth which was coming my way in the darkness. All this time, the city lay fast asleep around the prison, and there I was, thinking about the cypresses swaying in the wind. The footsteps sounded even closer. My blood was running wild and overflowing with one single question. Every word ever uttered, since the very beginning of the world, had lost all meaning for me. I had forgotten about my theories. There was nothing else I felt inside but that fear of waiting, from one second to the other, for the door to open. Those who have never gone through a strain as unbearable as that cannot judge me. Because there are things which defy judgement unless you have felt them deep down in your own flesh, pondered them deep down in your own mind."

XXVII

"There was a time when I didn't concern myself with any of this. In those days I would have said that only a lunatic would fill his dreams with monsters. But the Inquisition ruined it for me, this pleasant lie.... You might have heard, perhaps, that once I invited some teachers and students to attend a demonstration I gave at the leaning tower of Pisa. I went to the top and dropped several objects of various sizes. I wanted to show them how the speed of descent worked. In those days, I was prepared to face anyone. Now, I'm old and wrapped up in memories."

"But you used to love beginnings, Galileo."

"I still believe that a beginning has a lot of beauty in it. But I've come not to think of myself as the purpose of time. I've no doubt that these rivers will flow just the same or perhaps even more beautifully after I am gone. Other summers will come and make fruit ripe. It's only that my hand will no longer be here to pick it."

"Others will."

"I envy them already."

"Others envied you, too. It's one of life's laws."

"I can understand that, but it doesn't lessen my sorrow when I think that one day we won't be strolling like this anymore. I look at these golden hills, and I see them bathed in a light which seems to be coming straight from my youth. In the distance, I can see red roofs and parched church walls. Look... I've visited most of these places, I've memories there; I've even come close to death there without ever knowing it . . . . Some people would want us to believe that this world could make sense only if we repented of our sins, but there, this is my sin: I am not ashamed of being a sinner. If it weren't for the earth, heaven would be worthless. I am convinced of it just as I was convinced, in my dream, that had I had some water, I could have had everything. The heat was scorching, it dried out the grass and gave it a reddish glow, making the leaves of the trees taste like ashes and driving animals mad with thirst. Springs ran dry, the earth was cracking, no clouds could be seen in the sky, and there was no hope for rain, either. The air was burning hot, and here and there because of the drought, fires would break out wreaking havoc with whatever was left. Judging by the attire of some people whom I saw not far away from me, crying for divine mercy, I realized they were Romans. Just as I was heading their way, I spied a drop of water which had miraculously survived. I bent over, my lips parched, to ease my thirst. I was instantly horrified. I had lost all resemblance to a human being. I was a mastiff, and a red-furred one at that, and right then it dawned on me that the Romans used to sacrifice a red dog to chase the demons of the drought away. Out of the blue, what started preying on me was not so much my thirst but the fear that I could be seen, chased, caught, and sacrificed. I tried to stay away from human settlements and walked instead through the undergrowth and the forest. The moment came, however, when I could no longer stand the thirst and I came out in search of water. A passer-by noticed me and ran after me, throwing stones in an attempt to hit me and knock me down, but fortunately there was a thorn bush growing nearby and I found shelter under it. But from my hiding place I could hear one of my persecutors tell the others: *One way or another this dog won't get away. It's destined for the fire. Didn't you see how russet it was?"*

"You're far more complex than I thought, Galileo."

"Well, I'll try to make things simpler. Sometimes I wish I could drain the days and the hours of all that happens and turn myself into an object."

"There are times, indeed, when I can feel some sort of renunciation in your words."

"Unfortunately, I don't seem to have much success with it."

"You've conceived of a moral which accounts for everything that comes your way."

"While Ecclesiastes says that this world is a valley of tears, I for one wish for nothing more than to roam in it, and even find, particularly in the summertime, enough reasons to pity those who have gone to heaven."

"Your statements are dangerous."

"So much the better. It's the comparison that matters."

"What comparison is that exactly?"

"That of my dares and my fears. But what about you, would you be up to facing the stake?"

"I don't know, Galileo. But we hardly ever wish to see in others what we want to fight within ourselves."

XXVIII

"We've talked about Nero and then I dreamt I was Nero."

"Did you kill, too?"

"I was giving a speech to the people of Rome before setting it on fire. They were listening to me as if they'd turned to stone. *When I look at you I feel the same disgust as if I were looking at a bunch of rats, and all I can think of is how in just a few hours the flames will have devoured you when I have burnt Rome down. Don't try to save your lives. I have sentries watching the city gates and anyone who attempts to escape shall be skinned alive. I want you all lined up like lambs on a spit. It's no more than you deserve. And stop trying to fawn around at my feet. I know your kind. You don't even have the heart to look me in the eye for fear I might read your thoughts. Had you attempted to murder me, I would have caught you and sentenced you to death, but at least you would have earned my respect. And perhaps, the moment before letting the beasts feast on you or even the very instant your flesh was being ripped on the arena and your blood bathed the sand, I would have forgiven you. But now you shall die a contemptible death. Because contempt is all you deserve. That's why, when Rome has been burnt to the ground, I shall have all the ashes collected and flung into the Tiber as a thing of utmost shame. Even your ashes are not worth keeping.* Afterwards I beheaded a few statues and replaced the heads of the gods with my own, then murdered some senators out of sheer boredom, saying: *The stronger one kills. And because he is stronger, he doesn't say: 'I've killed', but 'I've won'.*"

88

"This is how the Inquisition thinks, too."

"The morning after, I stared at the ceiling for quite a long while, wondering what the coming nights had in store for me."

"Perhaps, you've lost all faith in people, Galileo."

"In some of them, I have. I drank life to the lees. Even though you'll probably tell me again that I've lived my life cautiously. . . ."

"Galileo, did you know that Ignatius of Loyola aimed for military fame first? He was injured in the foot by a shell splinter. And so, instead of becoming a Castilian knight, he chose to be one of Christ's knights. Because that was the only army he could join, lame as he was."

"And what does that prove?"

"That for some people the earth really does not spin."

XXIX

"Last night I went rambling through the woods. It was quiet; the sky was deep, ablaze with stars. I dozed off, and then I heard a voice. *You had to choose between the stake and the scorn. And you chose the scorn. You preferred to be scorned rather than respected as a martyr.* 'People', I defended myself, 'can be divided into two categories: the ones who are forced to make a choice and the ones who pass judgment on the former. I belong to the first lot. But only those who have had to make a choice are truly able to cherish life.'

Ironic laughter rang above my words. Then a blast of wind rose and drowned all other sound."

"Our inability to use simple words may be yet another source of unhappiness, Galileo."

"I'm afraid that talking about death in simple words is not an easy thing to do. Simple truths belong to life. Standing here, breathing in the sweet scent of the summer grass, I believe there's no experience one cannot survive. One can never say: I have tried everything because there's always something left to try. My passion for the light is the protest of a man who's almost lost to it. Everything is so simple. Just like the disgust the inquisitors awake in me."

"Galileo, may I ask you to explain something to me?"

"What's that?"

"You might have reasons to believe that I'm a spy sent out by the Inquisition. Or you could just as well nurture other suspicions as long as I'm nothing more than a stranger to you. We have run into each other once before, but you were too troubled then to remember my face. Why is it that you can confide all this in me?"

"There are plenty of reasons. Perhaps the demon of polemics lives on within me despite the plight in which I find myself. Perhaps, after the long muteness which was forced upon me, I feel the need to speak again. Or I might not be as suited to solitude as I thought I was after all. But I think that the most honest answer is this: I am selfish. Or it could be that I don't have the heart to ask myself certain questions. I'd rather have someone else do it for me and hope that having done so, the air will clear, although I doubt it will do much good now. What I ought to be doing with the time I have left is to try to get rid of my nightmares."

XXX

"I had forgotten who I was. I found myself in front of a building which everyone seemed to be avoiding but I couldn't understand why. Someone came out of the building carrying a pile of wood which he passed on to me and told me to take it to a nearby public square. I headed for the place as instructed, and it astonished me that all other passers-by appeared to be shunning me. Upon my arrival, I saw a statue standing in the heart of the square, and so I placed my pile of wood at its feet as if it were a bouquet of flowers. The stone lips twisted into a grin, and a snake, burning like a candle, bit me. That very instant I realized that it was the statue of an inquisitor, the very same inquisitor who had forced me to recant. Overcome by shame, I made my way hastily along the walls and slipped out of the city. It was then that I heard the sound of footsteps behind. I thought I knew who it was and, without looking back, I asked reproachfully: 'Do you see what happens when I listen to you and allow myself to forget?' No sound interrupted the silence, and I thought the steps had gone away. When I heard the voice again, it was filled with the usual kindness, only even huskier and sadder this time: *It wasn't I who pushed you into this, Galileo. Neither is this that which I spoke to you about. One day you'll understand.*"

"Sometimes I have the feeling, Galileo, that to you the earth stopped turning the day you were made to fear for your life. You will have noticed it, too, I'm sure – the cruel, inhuman beauty of the sky standing high above the graveyard. It is sights like these that make a rebellious question surge from within: If the sun keeps shining and the flowers keep dotting the grass, why do our beloved ones die?"

"This rebellion of yours is not as abstract as you might think."

"Indeed, it isn't. In a way it, too, has brought me to where I am now."

"The truth is, I have no answer to your question. God alone holds the key to this mystery. And perhaps we too are to blame for it. While animals are content to just live their life, we waste our time with eternity, even though we are the only ones who know that all is doomed to perish."

"Yet I've heard of people who have died a simple death. Just sighed and closed their eyes."

"I've heard of them, too. They say they are wise. That might well be true. But I'm not. Even at this moment, I find death a repulsive mystery. But to understand certain things properly we must perhaps be guilty first."

XXXI

"Perhaps you're convinced that all that happened was inevitable."

"Would it have happened otherwise?"

"The way I see it, it depends on who fathered us: Cain or Abel. Perhaps this all comes down to destiny, too, Galileo."

"The misfortune is that there are quite a few prosecutors in this world. Far too many, in fact. You've barely opened your mouth to explain, when they've already picked up a stone and thrown it at you without having heard what you had to say. It is what makes them happy. To bring accusations, to insult you, to show their disapproval, these are all a question of honour to them. Do you want to know what I've come to understand these past few years? That misanthropy is a lesson one can never learn whilst being away from people."

"Have you by any chance turned into a misanthrope?"

"If I'm not one already, I'm very close to becoming one. And all the credit for still having doubts is entirely mine."

"What you're telling me is very serious."

"Whenever I walk around here, amongst these cypresses, I feel no bitterness about the commandment which orders us: 'Love thy neighbour.' I see only the grass, the warm stones, a sky so pure and full of promises that I forget about the rest. All anger leaves me then, and my melancholy dissipates."

"But not the memories of the Inquisition."

"When I put the prosecutors out of my mind, even these memories are lulled to sleep like lizards in the sun. It is then that I almost feel like never going back to society."

"The problem is, this option is available only to saints or failures."

"I could claim membership in the league of failures any day. I have reason enough."

"Don't be too hasty, Galileo. Failure is harder to bear than sainthood."

"Now, isn't it time you told me who you are, at last?"

XXXII

"Let's leave this question aside for a while. You'd better tell me if Ana has been back in your dreams."

"Not really."

"What do you mean 'not really'?"

"I was digging out the root of a cypress. I had made quite a pit, but I couldn't tell what I was looking for. Suddenly I hit something hard, metallic. I cleaned off the dirt, and there before my eyes was a glittering golden chest. It was unlocked. I raised the lid and saw inside a manuscript written in a language I wasn't familiar with. While skimming through it, trying to unravel the mystery, I heard Ana's annoyed voice: *Galileo, this manuscript should have seen the light of day only in a particular place. This is the Iliad he was carrying around in his golden chest.* And, then, everything went completely dark."

XXXIII

"Then I met you, and I told you that there were people whose glory stemmed from pain, but it didn't justify the pain."

"It has been said that Giordano Bruno's real contribution was not his Latin writings, but the pride he brought to his defiance of the Inquisition."

"And who says that?"

"People do. And it is people again who say that the stake shall weigh more heavily on the history of mankind than a whole library. Just as Socrates' death will, too."

"But why did they have to die the way they did?"

"It's not that they needed to die, it's that they didn't die in vain."

"It's just a matter of phrasing."

"No, it isn't. Because a stake which has burnt in vain doesn't shed its light on anything. It merely leaves a stain. That's all it does."

"A stake is monstrous anyhow."

"It is, Galileo, but it can be both monstrous and futile."

"Don't you think it takes even greater courage to live and suffer than to be devoured by the flames of a stake? Even if history remembers only those who burnt to death and ignores those who faced life."

"So according to your logic, the wronged ones are the ones who nursed their wounds."

"You know full well that I am right."

"Well, that's just it, Galileo, I'm not convinced. Socrates' death may have taught us more than his philosophy. And don't forget what happened shortly after that. His body had not so much as been lowered into the grave when Athens rose up against those who had set up the trial and pronounced the sentence. No one would offer even a piece of wood to the three accusers so they could light their fires. Meletus was stoned to death. Anytus was exiled. Does this not prove that through Socrates' death, his opponents achieved nothing but the hastening of the immortality of his work?"

"Yet there may be martyrs who, at the last minute, would have chosen to remain anonymous but happy."

"They followed their own path. And besides, we cannot recant everything. "

"See, to me things are simpler. There is the Inquisition and then there is the sun which warms these hills and warms us, too. I want to hold on to this feeling of joy and listen to the rustling of the cypresses. Is my joy so great a crime? Do you really have to reproach me for it? Why can't it be different?"

"Of course it can, Galileo. The problem is that this is about us having to say no to the Inquisition, and sometimes the only way to say no is by paying the highest price. Crito told Socrates while the latter was imprisoned: 'Your death is undeserved' to which Socrates replied: 'I would deserve it if I gave up now.'"

"I envy Sisyphus. I wish I were sentenced to climb these hills for all eternity."

"Then why do you still care about what people say?"

"Perhaps I shouldn't care anymore. My own company has become burdensome to me as it is. An inquisitor courteously invited me to set a stake on fire. 'To prove that your recantation was wholehearted, Galileo. Do not fear, the man on the stake is just a straw man, a puppet.'"

"When did you have this dream?"

"It doesn't matter . . . . I was standing earlier under a crab-apple tree. I was eating some of the sour windfalls I had found in the grass, staring at the haze made so tremulous by the heat. Moments like these, I don't need any proof of anything at all anymore."

XXXIV

"Whoever mistrusts the necessity of truth ends up demanding it of others, Galileo. A world incapable of producing martyrs is a world incapable of defending the truth. This is where the problem lies. It's not a question of whether you were a martyr or not but whether you *were capable of being one* – in other words, if you were capable of advocating, at all costs, the truth of an idea in which you believe."

"I shall hold strong to my conviction that there's no greater failure than death."

"But there is. A life without faith."

"For the love of God, but I believe with every fibre of my being that I am alive! Old as I am and nearly one foot in the grave, I cannot hear big words about the heroism of dying without pitying those who utter them. What it means is that they have not yet discovered the wonderful mystery of living, of enjoying the sun, enjoying the summer. You'd rather have the glory of the stake? You are all welcome to long for it. To me, what glory looks like is this day we're living."

"And which is to wane soon."

"The world would have mourned, perhaps, for a Galileo Galilei who turned to ashes. But a living Galileo vexes it. Why, since he was so close to the stake, why didn't he go on it? Why does he enjoy roaming these hills when he was given the chance of being a martyr? Why did he decide it was more important to not become a victim after all he had ever done had held no other purpose, why did he change his mind at the last minute and choose to live instead? All it would have taken was to drain his mind of everything which might have pushed him into regretting that he was to die. Just a grain of indifference and he could have landed amidst the blazes ensuring his immortality. Why did he have to back off at that very instant? Glory was right there where he could have reached for it and yet he squandered it, trading it for the few years he may have had left to live. So intimate was he with the sweet scent of grass that he was frightened, naturally, of the smell of burnt flesh. But because of this, the world lost a saint!"

" . . . and gained a man, you mean."

"So this was the argument I didn't have, the ashes. If I'd had that, there'd have been nothing with which to reproach me."

"Could you really have told those willing to pay any price for their ideas that they were making a mistake?"

"No, I couldn't."

"Could you prove to them that their death wouldn't make any difference?"

"No, I couldn't. These are decisions no one can make for us. Judging others does not appeal to me."

"Or to be judged, either.

"My judges expected of me to show no concern about their threats, didn't they? Had I done that, they could have made an example of me. But I'll admit it again: all I thought about was my life. My life and nothing more. Everything else became inconsequential to me. My one and only concern was about my life. Is that terrible? Unforgivable? Are they disappointed that I'm alive?"

"What they are disappointed about is that you could swear on the Bible about something in which you didn't believe. You said: 'I, Galileo, seventy years of age, recant, curse and detest the error and the heresy that the earth moves.' "

"Precisely."

"And you did that on your knees."

"That's how they made me do it."

"And you agreed to it."

"That I couldn't fight, I realised it would have been the last straw. But how could you possibly understand that, you who've never taken any risks? My fear doesn't earn me your forgiveness. The only way to be worthy of your compassion would be for me to have acted heroically, no matter what the cost. It is the truth, admit it. Why aren't you saying anything? Well, thank you, but I have no need for compassion. My life is my life. And besides, I didn't put anyone in danger by refusing to die."

"I see you're angry. Now please calm down."

"Let me tell you that I'm sick and tired of people who ask the world to beget martyrs just so they can fulfil, through others, their own need of heroism."

"Well, in my case, this is not it. You'll see for yourself."

"Still, there are plenty of those who wish it. Pray tell, is it my fault that the Inquisition exists?"

"No, it isn't."

"Then you can all spare me your scornful pity."

XXXV

"Perhaps I shouldn't be telling you about my other thoughts, Galileo. I can see that I'm beginning to annoy you, and I wouldn't want you to add me to the 'prosecutors', as you call them, who are making your last years taste so bitter. However astonishing it may be to have a stranger tell you such weird things, there is something between us which equally connects and sets us apart. I too think with my heart, Galileo, even if my intransigence might have led you to believe that my way of thinking is too dry, blind to the fact that truth is not the only foundation of life. It is just that my heart has hardened because of circumstances which deny me all solace, unlike you, who can still be comforted by watching the mourning silhouette of the cypresses turning white. Perhaps it is the balance between love and despair, to use your own words, which is decisive in any destiny. For you, I've realized, love has rebelled against despair, and so, for the time being, it can offer you some kind of comfort, not counting the nights. For me, however, things are exactly the other way round, Galileo. I find myself incapable of feeling love for almost anything at all. My balance has been disrupted, and it has left me desolate, naked, faced with the choice of either putting up with whatever I have left, which is despair, or

101

going mad. I don't know how long a human being can last without solace of any kind, and so perhaps this is what I have come here to find out by talking to you. Listening to you, I'm trying to figure out what it is one can still hope for after having lost what is most precious to them . . . ."

"What do you think I've lost? The appreciation of those who would have preferred me to be a hero?"

"No, that's not it. You see, Galileo, you are not just anybody. Your name travels to other countries. God endowed you with gifts He denied others. That's why people have expected of you more than of themselves. You must understand this. They wanted you to do what they themselves never dared. And I make no secret of the fact that I am in the same situation myself. I've never dared to stand against the Inquisition. Quite the contrary, in a way, I've even served it."

"In what way?"

"It doesn't matter. I detested the inquisitors in silence, without ever showing my hate. I was grumbling under my breath, and there were certain things I didn't have the courage to tell anyone. I locked them up inside for fear of giving myself away. Had they ever suspected me, they would have crushed me like an insect. They wouldn't have even bothered putting me on trial. Who was I? A nobody. I was not a threat as you were. And it was precisely because my soul was numb with fear that I nurtured such admiration for you all through your polemic with the Jesuits. I was delighted with your wit and your piercing words. Your pride was my revenge for all the humiliations I had suffered without a word. How beautiful your pride used to be, Galileo! You were as sly as a fox and as swift as a tiger. You knew how to bow in a way which made it clear to everyone that you were mocking them and that a gale of laughter was hiding right behind your humble words. Your polemic with the Jesuits was an extraordinary performance of wit and vanity. You made them bite their tongues in their effort to keep up with you. There may have been many who felt then what I did: huge gratitude that there were people like you who proved that the Inquisition was not omnipotent after all, and that certain truths could still be uttered or at least whispered. And then, out of the blue, our gratitude collapsed under your recantation which swept over like a cold wave and froze all hope. Bold and solemn, the Inquisition re-established its might. It was this dismay which bore the reproaches aimed at you, Galileo."

"Are you trying to tell me that my life was no longer my own?"

"What I'm trying to tell you is that our expectations had placed you high above your destiny. What we did was excessive, no doubt about it. But this excess helped us breathe more easily the air poisoned with dogmas and fears. We had placed you on a pedestal, Galileo."

"But never cared to ask me whether I aspired to become a statue."

"You're right. But I'm only trying to explain what happened. The instant you came off the pedestal to kneel before the inquisitors, we all felt betrayed."

"I turned detestable."

"You turned into one of us, Galileo. Fearful, concerned for your own life, willing to say whatever you were told to say. Your face was no longer a pleasant sight to us, because it mirrored everything which deep down we detested within ourselves or made us feel ashamed."

"Your words sadden me."

"But this is about something more than being selfish. People need role models; they want to achieve, albeit through others, what they are incapable of achieving themselves. That's why they went from awe to rebuke. You doubled their loneliness, you dispirited them by showing them that it wasn't just courage they lacked, but also a role model to believe in. When they reproach you for your recantation, it's not because they would have refused to do so. The source of all these reproaches is different. It is their bitterness that since Giordano Bruno, there has been no one else bold enough not to recant. You know too well, Galileo, that quite often vehemence is the offspring of love met with vexation. It's not unusual for us to find ourselves reluctant to give the time of day to those we once admired but who proved to be a disappointment to us. What you must remember is that you were not like the rest of us, and this is what makes everything different. You cannot be measured with the common yardstick."

"You expected me to offer more than I was capable of. And in the process, you forgot what matters the most. That life is the last thing one gives away."

"As a matter of fact, the most regrettable thing for those unable to forgive your recantation was that you proved to be too much like us. We are not heroes who never got the opportunity of showing their heroism. We are just frightened humans. We fear for our life so much that we wouldn't have even run the risk, as you did, of feeling the heat of the stake. We would have shrunk back from it long before that. But somewhere deep inside, we always believed that there still were strong people in the world whose spirit of sacrifice was greater than ours and whose pride knew no fear. The Inquisition had humiliated us for too long by instilling fear in us. We had this need, an almost instinctive one, to pit our pride against the Inquisition, a pride which would avenge us, defy it, and put it in its place. And so for quite a long while, this was the role you had to play."

"I was your instrument."

"Our instrument of despair, if you like. If only you could imagine the comments your polemics with the Jesuits gave rise to, the satisfaction we felt, the hope we nurtured. We admired you even when you used the Pope."

"He didn't rush to my defence."

"The truth is that you weren't totally honest with him, either. You offended him when you had a silly character impersonate him. But none of us blamed you for this. On the contrary, it was a delight to see you playing with fire. Your wit gave us shelter. That was why it was all the more difficult to see you grow meek and curse your heresies afterwards. We felt disappointed but more than that, we felt even more vulnerable to hazards, an even easier prey. Your recantation left us defenceless, Galileo. This was what they were not willing to forgive you. That through your weakness you revealed our own weaknesses to us. In fact, people were honouring you by admitting that they were far weaker without you. Until your recantation, we were convinced that the truth could be placed above our petty little fears. You took that beautiful illusion away from us."

"So it turns out I'm guilty of refusing to sacrifice myself in order to keep a lie alive. Doesn't it really matter to anyone that I was seventy years of age at the time of my recantation?"

"How is age relevant to what happened?"

"It is immensely relevant. At seventy it is very difficult to be arrogant. Your mind is not set on defiance anymore because you've understood that the one defiance you're after is beyond your grasp. When you've reached my age, you'll understand that it is far easier to be a hero in your twenties. At that age, you can afford to look death brazenly in the face. At seventy, however, that is impossible. And you grow shier when it comes to truth as well. Great truths, like the rotation of the earth, recede into the background. It is the small truths that come to the front. That your bones ache, that you feel a slight tremor in your hand, and that sometimes your vision gets a bit blurry. This is when you grow grateful for each day you're still allowed to live. That great love is closer to pain than to happiness is a revelation that awaits you only in your old age."

"I have had this revelation, and I'm not an old man yet, Galileo. For me, it all started with a love story with an unhappy ending."

"Was it a woman?"

"Yes, it was, but I do not want to talk about myself. I'm not the one who matters."

"I myself don't matter anymore either. I've turned into a memory. People still need me only so that they can judge me. Beyond the trial, I'm no longer a matter of interest to them. They'll keep on saying, just as you do, that we each have our own truth by which we will be judged one day. And all I could tell them is what I have already told you, which is that I don't think my death was needed as confirmation that the Inquisition is abhorrent. One less victim doesn't make it acceptable. It stays the same even if I can still watch the sun and the sky."

"Admit, at least, that your recantation was capable of stirring confusion."

"Even God Himself was on their side. They never stopped calling His name. I would have been all alone on that stake up there. Should I feel guilty of this, too? The stake was not a general theoretical subject there; it concerned me."

"To my mind, Galileo, I've come to understand that sometimes in order to move forward, honesty may take parallel paths, ones which never meet."

"Because there is no one single truth. Each has their own truth."

"You keep talking about the cypresses, the summer, the light. This is your truth. But those judging you have their own, too. They find it difficult to accept that nothing can stop the Inquisition."

"And what is your truth, presuming you have one?"

"I've already hinted at it."

"Sometimes I get the feeling that I am caught between two inquisitions. One asking me to recant and the other asking me to account for my recantation. And, trust me, I'm tired of bumping into courts wherever I go."

"Is that why you're always running away from people?"

"The Inquisition would take a dim view of my talking to you. If they found out about it, they would forbid me to leave the house. They would force me to recite, under surveillance, the seven psalms and nothing more."

"It doesn't bode well for any of us if you prefer the company of cypresses to that of your fellow humans, does it?"

"Ever since I was released by the Inquisition, I've done nothing but explain why I didn't want to die. Those discontented with my being alive are nearly as unyielding as the inquisitors who threatened my life. This is not an easy thing to live with."

"Let me point out that you're still the forester caught between the moment of waking up, terrified to discover the vipers asleep next to him, and the moment when they get off the bed, drawn to the scent of warm milk. Trapped between these two moments, you are afraid to accept the truth."

"Am I not, at my age, finally entitled to a truth of my own? It seems I'm no longer able to satisfy everyone's demands. But I could at least try to make peace with myself. And it's no use asking me to be inhuman and not care that I haven't much time left."

"I'm afraid, Galileo, that you don't truly know what solace is. It's no good trying to pretend you can explain everything."

XXXVI

"When I listen to you, I feel the same helplessness which used to come over me whenever I tried to explain my understanding of piety to the inquisitors. No sooner had I opened my mouth than one of them would snap and frown at me: 'Has anyone ever seen anything like it? To talk to God using the same words one has for a lover?' I realized then that it was not only futile, but also dangerous to say anything more . . . . Your reproaches now stir in me the same feelings. I can hardly avoid saying 'I might' these days, and I feel inclined to use it more and more often as there are fewer things I'm certain of. But you, on the other hand, you don't seem to have doubts. You had your decision: 'If Galileo Galilei had wanted our respect, he shouldn't have been afraid.' Does it surprise you then that your reproaches sound to me like noise I long to retreat from, wishing to be deaf to anything but the wind? And, please believe me, it is not my wounded pride which is driving me away. It's questionable whether there's a trace of vanity left in me at all. It's solely the urge for peace that pushes me to it."

"Doesn't this urge worry you, Galileo?"

"It did, in the beginning. I wasn't used to being alone. But when I got wind of the commotion I had caused, a deep sense of indignation came over me. I understood that nobody was really interested in what I was thinking. I was a mere 'case'. And what was more, a case that was closed, dead and buried. 'Galileo? Oh, yes, the one who recanted . . . .' My reaction at the time was a mixture of bewilderment and rage, and the compassion of those who showed me pity looked like immodesty to me. I told myself: 'I wish the Inquisition would take them away, just for an hour. That would be enough for them to stop blaming me for having missed the wonderful opportunity of leaving some venerable ashes behind!' As time went by, I successfully mastered my vexation, and when my penance was over and I was allowed to leave the house, I tried to explain myself. A rather futile attempt, unfortunately. My interlocutors were all genial listeners who would cast a furtive glance around to see whether we were being watched, but who never cared to understand how it felt being in my place, not even for a second. This was a huge discouragement, a blow even heavier than the one delivered by the Inquisition because it was unexpected. In the presence of the inquisitors, it was natural for me to feel lonely. The flame of the candles sizzled like burnt flesh and the inquisitors themselves, clad in their purple robes and seated in their imposing thrones, seemed to be floating in the solitude of the hall as if inside an aquarium. I summoned all my efforts in an attempt not to let my face betray either fear or shame, but the moment I knelt, my mind emptied instantly. Anyway, I never expected what was to follow. If only you could understand this, then you'd also understand why I don't feel like leaving this place. When you go back to your own work, there will be no one left to ask me for explanations."

"Is this what you want?"

"Yes, it is. I want to be left alone. I've realised that everything I love brings me nothing but despair, and so what point is there in tormenting myself any further with the thought that instead of being understood, I am at best excused? Nobody is willing to understand that I've become so vulnerable that I have no strength left to fight for principles. I could do with some less worn-out words for what my heart feels with such clarity, but I don't seem able to find them. Why don't I tell you instead about another dream of mine?"

XXXVII

"She advanced through the cypresses in silence, her hair filled with sun and her arms loaded with grass. I didn't dare move or say a word. When she stopped next to me, she told me in the most natural voice, as if we were carrying on a conversation from the night before: *Have you noticed the olive trees laden with fruit?* The lizards lying on warm stones around us were sleeping in the sunlight. *Their dreams*, she said, *are flooded with light; they are not like yours.* I felt the need to be tender. 'I missed you.' She reached out her soft white hand to me, and her gesture moved me so much that discarding all caution that I might ruin everything, I asked her: 'Where have you been wandering since I last saw you?' She didn't answer, but her silence suggested she was concealing something . . . . Then she started telling me an old story about how an oracle had predicted Alexander's death to him. Upon hearing it, the king had taken the *Iliad* out of his golden chest, asked for a harp to be brought in and for someone who could teach him play it. The people around asked him: 'What's the use of learning to play the harp when you're about to die?' Alexander replied: 'So that I can play the harp before I die. It was pointless for me to argue that these words had belonged, in fact, to Socrates. Ana wouldn't hear of it. *I saw him caress the strings of the harp with my own eyes, and while he was playing it, the sun went behind the clouds and the sea turned red. . . .'* Her last words made me plunge into another dream. I was sitting on a sun-baked rock, on a strange remote island, away from the world, somewhere amidst the sea. The waves were lapping at my feet, and I could see sharks fidgeting around in the idle blood-red seawater. If I failed to imagine paradise, I would be cast out of the island and thrown to the sharks. At first I thought that this whole paradise thing was a child's play. That all I had to do was imagine trees with branches straining under the weight of ripe fruit, soft tender grass, springs melting light and shadow. I thought I could even picture God Himself and find Him an agreeable face. But how on earth could some people be happy without any memories or any hopes to nurture? Despite my pains to find an answer to this question, I couldn't find any. Then someone hissed in my ear: *Now you know you're guilty, Galileo, don't you?* ' And once again I saw Ana. She was right where I had left her before, only the sun had set in the meantime. 'Don't you understand that I speak of the stake the way you do of Alexander?' I asked her, almost brutally. Her hands shook gently in a soft white glow. And without a word she vanished – just when I wanted to ask for her forgiveness."

XXXVIII

"Sometimes, when I close my eyes, it occurs to me that time is born out of comparisons. Cypresses rustle in the wind, a piece of fruit falls to the ground, a cry is heard, a roll of thunder heralds the coming of rain, a bird screams . . . these are noises I've heard so many times before, they are alike and yet different. Because now they sound different to me. Can you picture Oedipus, a young man haunted by melancholies? If he's young, he must be king . . . . When I was a child, I used to lie in wait, together with some other children, to watch a young bear steal wild boar cubs. The moment it heard the wild sow's grunts, it would climb up the bent trunk of a nearby tree and sink its claws into the mushrooms growing all over the tree bark. One day, someone came up with the idea of cutting out the bottom part of the mushrooms. Having done this, we resumed our watching positions and waited for the bear to resume its play. Our exploit had a bestial outcome. The mushrooms gave way under the bear's feet, it collapsed and the sow dug her fangs into its belly, blood splattering all over the grass. But it is only now that I find this scene terrifying. I had put it right at the back of my mind."

"Perhaps compassion is a feeling one learns."

"I'm not all that certain about this. I stopped once in a town where the local doctor had been found hanged on a tree in the woods. He had been married to a woman he hated. A marriage of interest, I was told. Whenever he got drunk, his hands would start shaking, he would lie dead to the world and cover himself in his own piss. Some claim that such people don't kill themselves. And yet, what was it that drove the doctor to hang himself? Perhaps it was alcohol and hate that wore him out. Or was it something else that broke his heart? I must admit that the mystery of death had never seemed more obscure to me before. But what struck me the most was that nobody seemed to have any compassion for the doctor. They condemned his act of hanging himself as unchristian and denied him the right to be buried in the graveyard. They never cared to think that perhaps there had been something the man had not been able to put up with anymore and that he had found no other way out."

"To live well, one needs either reason or a rope, Diogenes the Cynical used to say. What do you think?"

"There was a time I would have said without hesitation: keep the reason and throw away the rope. But now I feel closer to Seneca's words. 'He who dies just because he is in pain is a coward; but he who lives merely to brave out his pain is a fool.' I even went through a crisis. I had just ended my penance, and I was out for a walk. I was dizzy with the light in the streets. I had longed for it for so long, watching at noon, from behind the curtains, the stump of a withered pine tree surrounded with nettles. A sense of foreboding came over me when I saw the passers-by avoiding me. They looked away when I walked by. But then I saw a former pupil of mine and breathed a sigh of relief. I happily walked up to him, ready to embrace him, only to find out that, to my astonishment, he was in a hurry to cross the road. I let out a curse and returned home disgusted. My head was spinning with all sorts of raging thoughts. I had done my penance by conscientiously reciting the required seven psalms under the icy watch of the woman guarding me, but to do another penance now because people were cowards – that was too much to bear. In those moments of sheer anger, I felt capable of a gesture which would be a slap in the face of my contemporaries. What followed was that I chose to subsist on venom and endure such dreadful sorrows that it almost drove me to asking the Jesuits, same ones I had gibed at, for forgiveness."

"Do you blame those who kill themselves?"

"No, I don't blame them, but I don't approve of them, either. I simply don't understand them. All I can say is that the life instinct may wear out, too. But, in case you might want to study the suicide issue, I'm far from being the right teacher. I had the opportunity of doing it, in a most heroic manner, by refusing to recant, and I failed to seize it. "

"And yet, doesn't this fleeing away from the world resemble a suicide?"

"People have nothing to offer me anymore. Still, the thought of death is like a stone-cold wall I cannot approach without recoiling in fear."

XXXIX

"Galileo, would you believe me if I told you that you acted as only a wise man would have done?"

"No, I would not. Nor do I advise you to say so. On the contrary, today I wish to hear all the bad things they say about me. I slept well, I had no nightmares, and I feel light and serene. I haven't felt so peaceful in quite a long while. I feel as if I've lived through a storm. Do you believe me?"

"No, I don't."

"And yet it is true. Do tell me, did they use the word 'cowardice'?"

"Of course they did."

"Just as I expected."

"There's no need to get gloomy, Galileo."

"Who said I was? I'm as peaceful as I have ever been. And I'm all ears."

"I've experienced cowardice in forms much worse than you have."

"Really?"

"Really."

"Nothing comes close to a court of the Inquisition. If you haven't been there, you have never tasted disgust."

"Oh, yes, I have."

"Silence hanging as heavy as a dripping wet curtain and it is you who must give an answer. What will the answer be? 'I, Galileo Galilei, aged seventy years . . . .' That's the easy part. The worse one has only just started. The first words you utter may be fatal for you . . . . This is not an experience that can be imagined. All those accusing me of 'cowardice' don't know what they are talking about, trust me."

"I trust you on this. I know you aren't given to exaggeration."

"How can you tell?"

"I just can, Galileo . . . from Julia."

"Who's Julia?"

"She's a woman I loved dearly . . . . She rubbed my left arm with rosemary leaf juice and said in a grave tone in Latin: *bestarberte corrumpit viscera ejus mulieris.* 'What does this mean?' I asked her. Julia burst into laughter. 'There's no escape. You're under my spell now. I'll make you cry, you know.' And she was right . . . . A woman like Julia doesn't commit suicide over a trifle."

"Perhaps, I should do the listening today."

"No, Galileo. These are things I do not wish to discuss."

"No, you'd rather rummage through my soul instead."

"It was you who wanted to know what people say about you. You felt you had to justify your actions. And, as far as I can tell, you're not done yet. As a matter of fact, you haven't told me yet how you fooled the inquisitors. How your abjuration was only make-believe so that you could get away without believing a word of your recantation, even though you recanted with your hand on the Bible."

"My opinions were well-known. No one could have possibly imagined that I really doubted what I had held so far. A formal recantation was the wisest solution at the time. The Holy Office had already resolved that my theories were heresies and made its decision public by issuing an edict. They couldn't have backed off without falling into disrepute."

"The only way out was to bring you into disrepute."

"Accepting something that was imposed on me under threat showed even more clearly that my ideas were truly dangerous to the Inquisition. They admitted indirectly their apprehension of my beliefs. And there was no point in acting obstinately. I let them believe the polemic was over and they were the victors. But this made it clear as day that they had no argument left on their side. The only thing left at their disposal was to threaten me with the stake. The battle had moved onto another field. I was alone, and I had to stand up to a juggernaut crushing anything standing in its way."

"And you were convinced that it was wise to be prudent."

"Euripides said something to this effect."

"I could give you instead a quote from Machiavelli: 'The prudent always know how to pique themselves on the actions life has forced on them.' "

"I don't brag."

"You're too wise to go that far, Galileo. And once more, this isn't about you having saved your life by performing a formal recantation, as you call it. I would have done the same."

"Then why are we even discussing it? Because this is the key issue. Those claiming that I shouldn't have recanted implicitly reproach me for being alive, for living. I couldn't have had them both: not recant and keep my life. I had to make a choice. And truth be told, all this chatter about my 'cowardice' is just endless hypocrisy. Nobody has the decency to say it loud and clear that it would have been wiser of me to have died. They're all eager to say only that it would have been kinder of me not to have recanted. As if to say 'no' and simply walk away were a possibility. Don't you think that if courage means the strength to despise life, then courage is something contrary to nature? And can anyone explain to me why it is so undeserving to hope for life, to cling to life? As I told you before, my heroism, if I possess any, is to look at this blue sky and not suffer too much knowing that tomorrow or the day after tomorrow I won't be seeing it again. Up here on this hilltop, having climbed up from the valley where the air is humid and cool, the heat makes me fall into a deep and pleasant torpor. I walk through the sun-scorched yellow grass and I cannot get enough of it. Do I have to be ashamed of this as well? I hardly think that anyone can throw this in my face. And if they can, my scorn would be justified. Why is it that while they chat on my account nineteen to the dozen, nobody ever mentions the names of the inquisitors who forced me to recant? Nobody ever points the finger at those who, had I failed to recant, were ready to carry firewood to the public square, set fire to the stake and sing to cover my screams. Or at those waiting in the vaults of the Inquisition, their torture instruments close at hand. The palace of the Inquisition is full of innocents! They were merely doing their duty, weren't they? It was their job. They were only turning an honest penny. They had a task to carry out; they were executing orders. I alone was to blame for making them drag me along the hallways and afterwards, perhaps, clean up the ashes in the square, too. Who made me uphold a truth so inconvenient to the Inquisition? Since I had allowed myself to be so presumptuous, wasn't it only natural to bear the consequences as well? And, as to those who would have come to see the performance had I been burnt at the stake, they would have all been innocent, wouldn't they? They would have flocked in, some driven by curiosity, others goaded by pleasure, and still others out of sheer pity perhaps, to witness the unhappy ending of a heretic. And once it was over, they would have gone home to tell the absentees what had happened, all of them ready to admit that I had taken things too far, that I had supported my views much too vociferously, inciting the Inquisition which could not ignore the heresy or else they might have been forced to feel ashamed of their own docility. There had been far too much defiance in my conduct. Thereupon they were regretfully bound to admit that, after all, what I had done was only to make a rod for my own back . . . . They are all innocent, naturally! The only one to bear any guilt is myself. And now even a worm can parade its dignity and bravery, cursing and pitying me: Poor Galileo was afraid . . . ."

"I thought you said that you were peaceful today, and your soul was free from any bitterness."

"I am peaceful. But don't you think that a society that lives like this has no right to ask anyone to die? As a matter of fact, the greatest harm the Inquisition did me was neither the fear I lived there, nor the humiliation I was put through. The greatest harm came only afterwards . . . . The Inquisition ripped a veil off my eyes. It made me see all the dirt a human soul can shelter."

"The world passes shallow judgments on you, Galileo. And I must admit that for a while I myself oversimplified things too."

"Some have opined that I got off quite lightly . . . although I set a bad example . . . . Why am I not allowed to love and be desperate for myself? Do I really have to be guided in everything I do by what others will say about it, by the impression I bestow on them?"

"No, Galileo, you don't. Nevertheless, you should consider that, at least in our heart of hearts, we must place a truth between us and the Inquisition."

"And what would this truth be?"

"Everything you say about life is true. But it so happens that the Inquisition took this perfectly natural fact, that human beings cling to life, and derived a vile conclusion from it. They understood that all they had to do was to resort to a few death threats in order to impose their dogmas. Thus any abjuration becomes, against the abjurer's will, an invitation to the practice of terror as a method of persuasion. Your recantation, Galileo, was among the greatest triumphs of the Inquisition."

"But it is not the ones who end up recanting that are to blame. They find themselves in a bind and they need to be selfish. Unless they defend their life, they will lose it. The harm done shouldn't be sought in the 'cowardice' of those made to abjure."

"Most certainly not. But allow me to carry on. What I'm about to tell you now is not something I've heard from other people. These are thoughts which, after Julia killed herself, kept nagging me all through the nights when I couldn't sleep a wink . . . . It was then that it became clear to me that the Inquisition has a keen interest in not relying on instruments of torture alone. If all it did were ceaseless torture, its power would be fragile. That's why it needs us to affirm its power through the fear which drives us to absorb its ideas. This way the Inquisition is not simply a police force separate from those it intimidates . . . . It becomes more than just the official way of thinking; we assume it as our own to stay clear of the danger. To be more precise, Galileo, the Inquisition, gifted as it is with a diabolical instinct, realised that it could cripple your soul without having to go to the trouble of pulling out your fingernails. All that is required is to scare you into saying only what is permitted. Afterwards you will gladly say whatever it wants to hear.

You will convince yourself there is no other way. You need a place to work, to publish books, to search the stars. What's the use of exposing yourself to hazards? You run the risk of landing at the stake while all the others, having been far wiser than you, will, at most, venture to commiserate with you under their breath. And the more natural the hypocrisy, dictated by the conviction that there is no other solution, the more powerful the Inquisition. In reality its ultimate goal is to proclaim, in its magnanimity, the end of physical terror, to give up the instruments of torture, to boast that it emptied the jailhouses and to reign only through our zeal to prove ourselves wise. This is what it aspires to achieve. To move the instruments of torture from its inquisitorial vaults and into our souls. Only then will its work really be complete. It will cease being the abomination it is because it will rely entirely on our self-scrutiny."

"I see we're going around in circles. We keep coming back to the exact same spot."

"Or to the exact same evil, Galileo. While we're having this conversation here surrounded by the cypresses, it's likely that more stakes are being erected."

"Since the world is cut out with crooked scissors, why shouldn't I content myself with being selfish and care only about my old age?"

"Because you feel the need to tell me about your nightmares. You don't think that has escaped me, do you?"

XL

"Not even the gods can change the past. You said it yourself, Galileo. So we'd better just stick to meanings. All inquisitions have relied on our ability to comfort ourselves after whatever befalls us."

"It's the nature of the beast."

"It appears that we possess an extraordinary capacity to find solace. After Julia died, I was so broken-hearted that I was convinced I would not survive her. Later on, I fell back on all sorts of pretexts to survive her. I told myself that first of all, I had to find out how she had died. Then that I had to avenge and somehow atone for her death. And look at me now. I can even talk about Julia's death . . . . So, we'd better stop mocking Nero."

"I'm not sure I see the connection."

"When Poppaea passed away, the grief-stricken Nero went out, and whilst roaming the streets, he came upon a young man whose appearance he found so oddly reminiscent of his deceased wife that he brought him to the palace, had him castrated and married him. Those who can replace one truth with another with such ease are either mad or virtually divine . . . . As for the rest of us, all we can do is try."

"Perhaps, but we cannot all match the cynicism of that Sforza countess who, while rebels were besieging the castle threatening to murder her three sons whom they had taken prisoner, climbed up the walls and flashed her womb at her enemies with the words: 'I possess the instrument to make more.'"

"I didn't know the story."

"It was a popular story in the taverns some years ago."

"Galileo, are you sure you don't want to go back to the joys of a pleasant life?"

"I don't think I can do that anymore. The world is filled with ugly surprises."

"You used to be such a carefree man. Fortune's spoiled child."

"Sometimes I sit and wonder what exactly it was that made me see the world in a different guise. Was it the shadow of the stake? Or what I found out afterwards?"

"It could be just your age. You pointed out that the recantation happened when you were seventy."

"Among the numerous other weaknesses that old age brings, it 'bestows' on us a better view on certain things which, luckily, would have passed completely unnoticed before. After so many years of perusing the sky and calculating the movement of the stars, it is only now that I have found out that at noon the sky is pale, young and careless but it ages when the evening sets in . . . . Once, if I was cold, all I had to do was to stretch out my hands to the fire. The warm blood would put me instantly in a good, happy mood. Now, however, everything is different. Sometimes even the light which I love so dearly is like a memory of a promise. This happens especially at noon when the cypresses flicker in the midday sun. Perhaps it was my lot that at the end of an indulgent life, I should be so alone that there is nobody with whom to share this loneliness."

"Do you understand now why I keep saying to you that whether you like it or not, everything has acquired with you a meaning which is simply beyond you? This has become bigger than you, Galileo."

"Yet deep down there is no tranquillity . . . . I did want to tell you that I followed Ana because I was intrigued by her sudden disappearances. We reached the plateau where we had been before; then we went closer to the desert and the sea, and she stopped there, in the narrow lee of a valley. It was a small oasis with a grave in the middle, a grave overgrown with herbs and flowers which gave off a poignant scent. It was a place of light and solitude which only the birds would disrupt when frightened by so much silence. A clump of old eucalyptus trees, heavy with the heat of the sun, cast a patchy shadow over the grave. The face of a young, imperious-looking man, with flowing hair was carved into a rock overgrown with herbs . . . . I recognized him. So it was in this oasis that Alexander's tomb lay . . . . Yellow flowers, growing wild, were besieged by hornets. Close by there was a straw cottage, blackened as if by rain . . . . Then I saw her eyes for the first time. Eyes too big for her face, blazing, wet and glowing, only to turn sad, almost sore in an instant. I could see her lips moving imperceptibly. I could even hear a murmur, but failed to recognise what she was saying. When I moved closer to her, I realized that Ana was reciting verses from the *Iliad* . . . . Instantly my eyes started aching from the bright sunshine and I could hardly see anything anymore. The light turned black."

XLI

"Have you had any more dreams?"

"I was up on the stake with my hands tied up and no sooner had a flame broken out than all of a sudden a heavy downpour came down and instantly put out the fire. The inquisitors were angry. They brought in people carrying torches to dry the stake and set it on fire afresh. But the rain put it out again and again. Trees and crops began to rot under so much water; the road disappeared under the puddles; the birds flew about frantically and people gathered round the stake, full of wrath. They were waiting for all this to come to an end so that they could harvest their wheat which was rotting in the fields and driving them into starvation. *Galileo, do you want all of us to die instead of you?*, one of them shouted at me. 'What would you have me do?' I asked, as they had let my tongue loose. *Pray for the rain to stop and the stake to burn so that we can get it all over with.* 'Why don't you ask the inquisitors to give up?' I asked, vexed by all the hurry. *They say their mission is to kill, yours to die, and that of the wheat to give bread – and you're obstinately disrupting the natural order of things.* 'The stake can never be a part of the natural order of things. Neither will I pray for my own death.' *Then you should curse, Galileo; maybe something will happen eventually.* And they stood staring at me in silence, waiting for me to die."

"Your nightmares are becoming more and more weird. You do the Inquisition's job yourself, Galileo."

"Nobody is willing to think of me otherwise than as someone threatened by a stake."

"Except for Ana, of course."

XLII

"I followed her again into the oasis by the sea. And again I listened to her reciting the *Iliad*. Eventually she noticed I was there and came up to me. I thought she would be angry, that she would reproach me for spying on her. Instead, she asked me in her soft husky voice: *Are you sad*? And she caressed my hands. 'No, I'm not', I answered as if I wanted to apologise for contradicting her. *And, yet, you look down*, she insisted. 'I'm only tired . . . .' I could see her eyes now. The same extraordinary eyes, so full of sun and sorrow. I could hardly bear to look at her. She glanced up at the sky and said: *See how old this sky is? As old as I am . . .* A few moments later she added: *When it happened, the birds of the desert cried out, the horses were snorting and kicking the sand with their hooves . . . .*' I didn't even need to ask her what she was talking about. 'Did you love him?' *I did*, she nodded. *I loved him as no other woman had ever done. And while other women were mourning him, I stood there frozen, listening to the rustling of the sand and the crashing waves . . . . This is how I spent my days and nights. After they buried him whilst reciting fragments from the Iliad, his closest chieftains gathered round the grave crying out his name and that of Achilles, and then everybody was gone.... I watched the horses disappear into a cloud of dust in the distance and then I was all alone, just the*

desert, the sea and myself . . . . I wished I could have cried like one
of those women who wiped their tears, and with their eyes still wet,
attempted a smile . . . . But I remained unchanged even after the
birds which had been flying around in circles for a long time had
gone away . . . . Then one night I thought the time had come for me
to leave. . . . 'What's your real name?' I asked her. She gazed at the
blackened straw cottage. *What difference does it make now? I'm*
not who I was then. She was facing the sun and an unbearable light
streamed from her eyes. I asked her: 'So this is why you told me
once that we share a scar?' She took my hand and we walked until
we reached a sycamore forest in the middle of which I could see a
fire burning. A wild scent I had never smelt before was floating
around the fire. It was only then that she answered me: *The*
beginning of wisdom is never easy."

.

XLIII

"You seem to have really lived all this."

"I did live it. I even saw some snakes sleeping on the warm
rocks, and I wanted to crush their heads with a stone, but a
stranger stopped me. *Wouldn't you rather have them recant,*
Galileo? I thought he was mocking me. 'What do you mean, have
them recant?' *I mean have them deny their calling.* 'But why waste
time?' I answered. 'I might as well kill them right now.' *This is more*
important, Galileo, the stranger added, his voice even. *'Making*
them deny their calling is far more important. Even when they're
dead, they would still inspire fear in you. But if they recanted, the

128

sight of their heads would arouse in you nothing more than repugnance. Then you could kick them aside as you would a clump of plants which are standing in your way. After the stranger vanished, I remained in the shade of the cypresses, crushing between my fingers the yellow leaves which had floated here on the wind and pondered on the words I had just heard . . . . Why are you so quiet?"

"I'm listening to you, Galileo. I'm trying to guess what is hidden in your soul."

"I think I'm not self-confident enough anymore."

"Self-confident or confident that you are right?"

"To be self-confident, I must be confident that I am right . . . or am I raving? Well, in that case I won't say anything about the inquisitor who raised his hood and let me see his face, the face of an ape wearing a shameless smirk. Thank goodness that you at least don't think me a maniac."

"No, Galileo, I don't think that. I only see you as you are."

"Which is what?"

"A subject of permanent debate for people. Just like the death of Socrates."

"One of these nights, I'm going to carve right through that rock."

"You've never spoken of this before."

"Someone once said to me: *Galileo, this rock is your destiny. If you have the courage, you must carve right through it, and you'll find inside that which you've been looking for.* And so I started carving eagerly and enthusiastically. One of the blows of my chisel, however, was followed by a scream. Then came a cry and shortly after a coarse shriek of laughter. I hesitated. *Why did you stop, Galileo?* 'There's somebody inside the rock. I heard him scream, cry, and then laugh.' *Didn't I tell you, Galileo, that this is destiny itself? This is no ordinary rock.* 'What am I supposed to do?' I asked. *Keep going if you want to find what you're looking for.*' I went back to carving but before long, I heard the scream again, followed by a cry, and finally the peal of laughter. That was when I threw the chisel away. 'I cannot hurt something that is alive.' *Suit yourself, Galileo, but there's no animal inside the rock, just destiny itself. It screams, cries, and laughs but never suffers any pain or feels any joy. If you aren't up to this now, you may return to it some other night.*' . . . I wonder what I would have found at the heart of that rock. Perhaps I'll never know."

"You have known love, Galileo. Isn't that enough for you?"

"Of course, I have known love."

"And you have known truth as well even though you abjured it."

"Every morning when I wake up, I'm filled with fear that I won't find anything where I'd left it the night before. But shortly after, I see that everything is in its place, and I calm down."

"In life, the only choice one has is between 'yes' and 'no'."

"It is 'yes' more often than not, that life requires of us. And I do want to say 'yes', by all means."

XLIV

"Last night, while I was sleeping, it snowed up in the mountains. In the morning when the clouds cleared up you could see the snow-covered peaks. This hasn't happened in summertime in a great many years. Then the sun came out and melted the snow away, and everything returned to normal."

"I don't think we can wander around here for too long, Galileo."

"You'll miss the peace of these cypresses."

"I daresay I will."

"People are far less convincing. Tell me, have you ever been up in the mountains at day break?"

"I have. Why do you ask?"

"When darkness fades away above the rocks, goats appear on the mountaintops, their muzzles all wet, shining in the sunlight as they make for the lake to drink water. Whenever I found myself around in moments like these, I was afraid to make a move lest I should blow away the magic. I have never seen clearer water than the water up there . . . . But there's something else I really wanted to talk about. Perhaps you know that Denocrates, Alexander's architect, intended to ask the Macedonian to allow him to build a huge reversed human shape holding a city in one hand and a well in the other."

"With enough water pouring from it to quench all human thirst."

"Exactly. The city was never built. But I saw the well when I followed Ana into the desert. The water sparkled in the sun. I wanted to bend over and drink, but as I did so I heard a jeering laughter. I got scared, thinking the water might be poisoned, and so I shrank back, resolved to suffer however much of a torture my thirst might have been. I picked up some leaves and chewed them, pulled plants out of the earth and drank their juice, but as time went by, my strength wore off. Then again I heard the sneering laughter. I lay on the ground facing the water and drank greedily even though I was certain I would die after I'd quenched my thirst . . . . That's all I had to say. Now, you talk to me about Julia. Was she beautiful?"

XLV

"I don't know whether she was beautiful or not . . . . What I do know is that I loved her. And that was enough for me . . . . Anyway, she had a special charm of her own and a naturally cheerful disposition in her good moods, which suited her so well. She was so spirited, surprising, and blessed with such zest for life that boredom could never survive in her presence. She loved dressing nicely, and whenever she bought new clothes, she would bounce about the house, asking me time and again with a truly feminine curiosity: 'How do you like it?' When I noticed a scar on her bosom, she grew sad instantly: 'It is ugly, isn't it? I wish you hadn't seen it.' I reassured her that there was no ugliness about it, but she wouldn't believe me. From that day onwards she would always try to hide it . . . . Perhaps because, in her heart of hearts, she was too sober and feared that too much gravity might erode the charm of a woman, she strove to give the impression of someone who took things somewhat lightly, who enjoyed playing with everything, feelings in particular. Among the first things she ever told me was that each autumn, she slipped into a 'sentimental coma'. She was terribly fond of the phrase 'sentimental coma' which she would utter with a mixture of irony and contentment. She warned me not to get too attached to her because I might regret it later. 'Next autumn I might fall in love with someone else and leave you', she explained in a tone which threw me off balance. Seeing my clouded countenance, she hugged me: 'Did you believe me? I was joking.' 'Stop making bad jokes', I told her, pretty peevishly. 'All right, I promise', she agreed. But she could not keep her promise for too long. Every now and again, she would remind me ironically that I had nothing to worry about until the following autumn . . . . She lived somewhere on the outskirts of town, in a neighbourhood where numerous tiny shops sold fruit, and her room smelt like an orchard. There was fruit all over the place, in baskets, in jars. 'I love fruit better than flowers', she explained. One day she complained that she was losing weight for no apparent reason. I myself had noticed that for some time she had been paler than usual, which made her black eyes look distinctly grave. 'You've had this mystical look in your eyes lately', I told her half in jest, half in earnest. We went to see a few doctors together, but none was able to tell her the cause of her weight loss. Seeing her so

133

concerned, frightened even, I tried to lift her spirits. She would listen to what I had to say but refuse to be persuaded, until the day when she simply refused to hear any more about it. She said in an affected laugh that all grave illnesses were in fact divine gifts with which only some were blessed. She went even further, concocting a personal theory which claimed that minor diseases lacked perspective, made one live on quack medicines alone, and never stop whining and complaining, whereas 'true diseases' were something else altogether! They made you happy whenever you had the chance to say 'I'm feeling better today'. How much of her words was fear and how much was pride I shall never know. In the end, she informed me with resoluteness which broached no argument that she would not see any more doctors. She was going to treat herself if needed. I told her that I wanted to marry her. She wouldn't even hear of it. 'How am I supposed to marry when I'm sick?' she objected. 'First, I want to get healthy. I do not wish to have a nurse for a husband.' And to put an end to the discussion, she added in a gaiety that I found jarring: 'Apart from anything else, I'll have to let an autumn or two pass, dear boy, to test my faithfulness. It would be immensely wrong to marry you now. What if you started nagging me for lying in bed, or if I slipped into a sentimental coma next autumn, never managed to wake up from it, and left you? We'd better wait.' I stopped insisting so that she didn't have to pretend anymore. When Julia set her mind on something, it was an impossible mission to have her change it. Besides, it was futile trying to convince her to see other doctors. She said she did not trust anyone and that she would not want to be the slave of a disease. I meant to pump her for secrets to see if there was anything she was keeping from me, but it was out of the question. 'I feel better', she would say, and the only explanation she offered was that women showed much more strength in the face of pain than men did. Sometime later she passionately took to magic, and one day I brought home some 'damned books' for her, thinking she might be interested. She was not aware of my profession, and so I lied to her that I had bought them from an antique shop, not to raise any suspicions. 'How come they dare keep such books in the antique shop and sell them?' she wondered. I made up a story of how I was acquainted with the antique dealer, and he had taken them out of a secret cabinet. 'It was a waste of your money. I'm not interested', she said and put them aside without even skimming through them . . . . What followed after that has no beauty in it . . . ."

"You've piqued my curiosity. What is it you're keeping from me?"

"Nothing, you'll see. Now, let's go back to you, Galileo. You've never told me what you think of Giordano Bruno."

"They always compare me to him, don't they?"

"Yes, they do. It is only natural."

"And to my detriment too, no doubt about it."

"That's true."

XLVI

"I was thirty-six when they burnt him at the stake in Rome. And it terrified me. After Socrates, no philosopher had suffered so brutal a murder. Burning Giordano Bruno to death proved that the Inquisition would not shrink from anything . . . . When, later on, I visited Rome and crossed the square where the stake had been erected, I pictured him amidst the flames trying to curse, his tongue tied . . . . The chill I sensed there I felt again only one other time, in the church of Sant' Onofrio at Gianicolo where I went to see the tomb of Torquato Tasso."

"I see that you've developed quite an obsession with all those who had something to do with the Inquisition."

"But Torquato Tasso was never harassed by the Inquisition. He harassed himself because of the disease that was increasingly ruining his life."

"Did you ever meet him? I used to love his poems."

"No, I never did. But I did hear quite a lot about him. He seemed to have suffered from a persecution mania. He saw enemies everywhere, people whose only goal was to see him dead and steal his manuscripts. He dreaded he would be poisoned and so refused to touch his food unless he had it tasted first. He believed he was being constantly spied on. One day, so the story goes, he as good as drew his knife upon a servant who had entered his chamber, taking him for a spy, and, had his screams not summoned the other servants to the man's rescue, he would have killed him. While living at a convent, he even accused the monks of seeking to poison him. He felt like a prisoner; he was given to crying fits and would often run away, not knowing exactly what it was he was running away from. He used to collect crucifixes and lived in constant fear that he would be denounced to the Inquisition, so much so that he ended up going of his own free will to the court of the Inquisition and confessing to sins he had never committed."

"And was he absolved?"

"He was. Then, he roamed for a long time in search of peace which he found only in his grave."

"They say that fresh flowers are always to be found on his grave in Rome."

"So it was for five centuries with Nero's grave as well. People give their flowers to poets and monsters alike. When I visited Sant' Onofrio, the church was closed, and I had to ask a priest to unlock it for me. He showed me Torquato Tasso's wooden inkwell, his death mask, and the crown of laurels he was to be awarded on the Capitol but didn't live to see. The priest's voice sounded hollow and sad inside those cold walls. People love taking pity on the misfortunes of others only as far as it serves them to parade their own sensibility, but this invariably happens after the death of those who are pitied. While he was alive, Torquato Tasso was so neglected that he was overrun with lice."

"What about Giordano Bruno? He too was a wanderer."

"I've seen him only once, in a dream. I was at a mill somewhere. I was working there as a sort of an apprentice. I was emptying the flour sacks while outside it was pouring with rain. Suddenly there was a knock on the door and a traveller appeared on the doorstep, his cloak dripping wet. When I raised my lamp to get a better look, I realised it must be him because of his haunted look. I got flustered and said: 'I'm not the miller; I'll go get him', but he was in a hurry. He shook his cloak, pulled his hood over his head and went out."

"He was fifty-two when he died. Do you think he did the right thing by sacrificing the time he might have had left?"

"It would be uncivil of me to pass judgement on him. I might have been able to do so in the past. I might have been able to tell you then as well that Giordano Bruno's life was filled with eccentricities. But now, no matter what I say, it won't look good. Don't ask me to have an opinion about this. I would be either dishonest or uncivil. The most I can do is admit that I lacked his ambitions."

"What do you mean?"

"As you may know, he had studied rhetoric, logic, and dialectic before becoming a Dominican friar. He was said to have preferred studying to prayer, and if so, I understand him perfectly. He was an avid reader of the classics and proclaimed himself a follower of Democritus, Epicurus, and Lucretius."

"You wanted to be a disciple of Aristarchus of Samos."

"It was not his studies that I had in mind when I told you that I lacked his ambitions. It was a pleasure for me to find out that although he spent most of his time in chanceries and libraries, he cursed the day when he had taken the vows. His southern blood made him daydream in his cell about beautiful naked women dancing and swaying their sinful hips before him. When he was about to turn thirty, he resolved to stop fighting the temptations of the flesh and gave up the frock – only to take it up again later, then renounce cloister life once more, determined this time not to stay away from the women he was fond of, as the rumour went, far more than he was of philosophy. He boasted that he had lain with more women than Solomon himself, and he is said to have been intimate with nearly a thousand women, according to the Bible. His tongue was sharp and a cause of vexation for many."

"Well, Galileo, you weren't far behind him either, you know."

"The difference is that he thought of himself as entrusted with a supernatural mission. He wanted to change the world and reform people. I have never nurtured such ambitions. He considered himself a magus."

"At first he retracted, too."

"But afterwards he retracted his retraction. Having listened to the sentence on his knees, he jumped to his feet and shouted at the judges: 'By giving me this punishment, your fear is greater than the fear I have to bear.' Compared to this defying vanity, my humility seems downright pathetic. It calls only for contempt, don't you think?"

"No, Galileo. You preferred to live."

"I've never been afraid to admit that all my hopes have always belonged to the part of me which recanted."

"It occurred to me that your recantation may have actually carried a more serious moral than just the assertion that the earth is spinning. The Inquisition never realized that."

"What do you mean?"

"By showing yourself humble, you were in fact insinuating the idea that all that ever matters happens here, on earth."

"It's what I believe. I can't simply start thinking otherwise. Watching the faces of the inquisitors, I realized that I was to share the same fate as Giordano Bruno, the difference being that I was not ready to face it, not even in my seventies."

"Didn't anyone advise you to flee?"

"They did."

"And?"

"And I said no. I didn't want to live in exile. Besides, I was hoping the danger would go away. I didn't expect that they would venture into a public encounter."

"It was what they needed. Things had gone too far. There were rumours that the Inquisition was afraid to lay hands on you. And they jeopardized its mythical omnipotence."

XLVII

"Ana took me back to that scented fire in the sycamore forest. *This fire burns only memories*, she explained to me. *It's a stake for memories. It turns to ashes only what you can remember. Will you dare?* I told her that I wouldn't want to part with my regrets because I wouldn't know what had happened to me anymore. She got upset and turned her back on me. Left all by myself, I began carving into a block of marble. At first I thought I would come upon myself asleep inside the rock for I caught sight of a man's feet. Then I could see the hands, the body, the shoulders. The face, however, remained undistinguishable, just an outline of the lips could be seen. However deep I chiselled into the rock, nothing else became visible. I paused for a second to catch my breath and wipe away the sweat, and that very moment, the lips moved but uttered no words. Then they moved again. And again. They moved as if to speak but not so much as a sigh could be heard. In vain did I put my ears to them. Infuriated, I picked up my chisel determined to smash them to pieces. That instant the lips moved again and this time a peal of laughter rang out over the clearing. It was the laughter I had heard so many times before, and yet I could not tell if it belonged to anybody in particular. I struck a heavy blow right at the opening of the lips expecting that blood would gush out. Instead, the lips opened wider and spewed an even more insolent burst of laughter in my face. I was gasping with rage, insanely and incessantly striking the stone lips while that jeering went on . . . . After that, I dreamt of a huge snake feeding on butterflies. It opened its mouth, and the tongue took the shape of a flower while the snake lay in wait, frozen, in the grass. Butterflies would sometimes stop nearby, but it kept stock-still, an unblinking stare in its eyes as if dead. Only the slightly trembling flower in its mouth betrayed its impatience. In the meantime, I had this explained to me: *Perhaps you know, Galileo, what it is they say about the bloodthirsty Tiberius? That he was top of the list of the outcasts, a list designed by himself. Yet, he never sentenced himself.* 'He did', I retorted, 'he exiled himself to the island of Capri, placing the sea between Rome and himself.' *He did it only because he had the passion of exile*, came the reply. *Those who have the power to pass death sentences only ever set examples through others.* This was when Ana returned. She offered me a glittering and fragrant flower necklace as a gift, which I was delighted and thrilled to put around my neck. My eyes lit up, and I felt like singing. I asked her without aiming for a particular response, why she had offered me the necklace. She gave me a look of pity and said: *I brought it to you because you disappointed me.* After a careful look at it, I recognized the flowers. They had been picked from Alexander's grave. *I've come to take you away,* she went on. 'Take me where?' *To listen to the sand birds of the desert.* Her words were soft and tender as her tone had been when she had recited from the *Iliad.* I was scrambling for a pretext to turn her down when I woke up . . . . Sometimes I wonder while listening to the howling wind at night: is melancholy really the best part I have left deep within?"

"I see you haven't really listened to me, Galileo."

"Summer alone may not be enough to make one happy. But it is enough to keep one from despair."

XLVIII

"The dream I had last night was dreadful. The ashes of the stakes had begun blossoming. When they saw that, the inquisitors decided to erect a prison to contain them and keep them out of sight. Big walls were built and the ashes were carried inside and locked into separate cells. Sometime later the walls began to lean and cave in. The ashes had not stopped blooming and the flowers were piercing through the walls. Seeing that, the inquisitors decided to build an even larger prison, one big enough to hold the

142

remnants of the old prison and stop the riotous expansion of the ash blossoms. All was in vain. Once in full bloom, the ashes could no longer be contained. They were just like lava flowing out of a volcano. Cracks appeared in the new walls too and the ash flowers pushed their way through them; the flowers were black yet graceful. Enraged, the inquisitors decided to have an even greater prison erected. Towns and villages were emptied in a hurry and houses, churches, and squares were abandoned inside a prison whose walls were far beyond what the eye could reach and which spread farther and farther, fleeing from the blooming ashes. They looked like two armies engaged in a battle. On one side there were those burnt at the stake, their ashes that is, and on the other there were the inquisitors making futile attempts to stop the marching of the ghosts. And so it was that the entire earth was in danger of being turned into an enormous prison, if that hadn't happened already, endlessly engulfing the ruins of one prison after another. I was in such a state of bewilderment that my first thought was to take a look outside and see whether I wasn't left inside the ever growing prison. No sound could be heard, and I had the feeling that in the meantime the city had been abandoned, that everybody, even my judges, had gone and left me there all by myself. Suddenly the tentacles of terror got hold of me at the thought that the ghosts of those burnt at the stake would ask me: *Why didn't you have the courage to face the stake, Galileo? Why were you a coward? Why did you recant? And since you were a coward, why didn't you flee the city together with the inquisitors? Why did you stay behind? Do you imagine that we are going to accept you as the only living human amongst us just because you were the only one to have recanted? You should have left, Galileo, you should have joined those you feared so much.* It took me quite a long time in the morning to recover my composure even though the celestial dome above was immaculately serene."

XLIX

"Please forgive my insistence, but didn't you waver at all, not even for a second, before deciding to recant, Galileo?"

"Well, let me tell you how it all happened . . . . In August, my latest book had been indexed and when I saw that, I sensed that something bad was afoot. The Pope had stopped defending me, leaving me at the mercy of the Holy Office. The Grand Duke of Tuscany who had risen to my defence on previous occasions was now seized by fear. My friends began avoiding me. But I still kept a grip on things. I hoped I would be able to overcome this impasse. And whether by accident or design, the moon too looked sick that autumn. People said this was a bad omen. My sleep, reduced to only a few hours a night, became torture; nevertheless, I managed to prepare my defence as I was resolved to produce new arguments in support of my ideas. It was only when I was summoned to appear in Rome that I became panic-stricken and had to admit that I was on the rack with waiting. Spring had already arrived, the air was suffused with fragrance, and as I was climbing the steps to the Holy Office, I saw the pine trees looking almost black in the daylight, an inauspicious sign, I thought. And I was right. They arrested me immediately. On my first night in prison, I dreamt that I was falling. I was falling into something that looked like an abyss. I could see the stars above me disappear and I waited for the inevitable moment when the sky would go out, too, like a candle in the darkness . . . . Because I fell ill, I was allowed to live under strict surveillance at the residence of the ambassador of Florence. During my first interrogation, they asked me if I pleaded guilty. I did not. A couple of days later, still hoping that things would come round, I agreed to tone down some of my texts. That wasn't enough for them, however. They sent for me, and the moment I entered that room, it became clear to me that they were determined to throw me on the stake. I could read it beyond all doubt in the cold, cruel eyes that were watching me. They declared me guilty of heresy. Just for a moment, I had it on the tip of my tongue to tell them that it was the heretics who had always pulled humankind out of the mire where it would have likely rotted otherwise. That Socrates, too, was a heretic. That Christ Himself was accused of heresy . . . But I lost heart . . . And so it ended. I fought as hard as I could."

"But unfortunately the Inquisition is like leprosy. It spreads and once you have it, you can't be free of it ever again."

"I went down to the valley today and looked at the houses scattered along the river. I enjoyed it. The sun was shining; the stones were burning hot. I saw a lad looking for something in the grass. 'Do you know who I am?' I asked him and told him my name. He had never heard of me."

"I see you're still not completely devoid of vanity, Galileo."

"I even stopped a man and asked him: 'Listen, do you remember Galileo Galilei?' The man looked at me, and I hoped he would recognize me, but he only shrugged and said: 'I seem to remember that there was a fellow who went by this name. It had something to do with the Inquisition.' So, yes, your verdict is accurate. I have become a leper."

"Do you still refuse to return to normal life, Galileo?"

"What can be normal to me now?"

"In a way, I do understand you, you know. What you're looking for doesn't exist anymore. And this goes for both of us."

"And what would that be?"

"Peace, Galileo. You and I, we are both doomed to never find peace again."

"Why shouldn't you? You'll love again. Or do you think you'll spend the rest of your life by Julia's grave?"

"I don't even know whether she has one."

"How come?"

L

"Do you remember my telling you that I had brought Julia some 'damned books' and lied to her that I had bought them from an antique shop?"

"I do."

"Well, as a matter of fact, I had taken them from a dump where they threw away books removed from the Inquisition's library."

"How did you manage to get in there?"

"I was working on a biography of Ignatius of Loyola, as ordered by the Holy Office."

"So you did rub shoulders with the inquisitors!"

"Not really. I didn't have much to do with them. All I did was go to the library, study, search for documents, take notes. I have to say that I was genuinely passionate about my subject. This Ignatius of Loyola was no ordinary character."

"I think I can guess what happened next."

"Those books were 'damned' indeed. I took my time returning them to where I had taken them from. But a prying neighbour, who had caught sight of them, wasted no time in going straight to the Inquisition to report Julia. The very same day, her house was searched and she was arrested."

"Didn't Julia suspect anything?"

"About what?"

"About what you were working on."

"Mine was no dirty work. I did not put up stakes, I did not set them on fire, and I did not torture people either. Even so, I held back from telling her. I was just putting it off. The name of the Inquisition was much too infamous. I feared she might despise me."

"And didn't you go and get her out of their clutches?"

"After Julia was arrested, I lived a waking nightmare for a few days and nights. Several times I set out to the Inquisition, determined to give myself up. But on my way there, I always ended up paralyzed with fear. I kept telling myself that they could not keep her there forever once they realized she had no interest whatsoever in all that nonsense. Never did I imagine that . . . . But naturally, this doesn't clear me of my guilt . . . . Once, eaten alive by remorse, I went there in the evening. Thinking that I had come to see to my usual business, the janitor informed me that the library was closed and that there was nobody there. Coward as I was, I said 'all right' and went back home . . . . The following morning I heard that Julia had thrown herself out of the window into the inner courtyard . . . ."

"Did they torture her?"

"I never found out. All my attempts to uncover any details were met with a wall of silence. And as I could no longer bear to cross the courtyard of the Inquisition on my way to the library, I had to tell them that I couldn't go on with my investigation . . . that the doctors had diagnosed me with a serious medical condition and I had to leave the city, to straighten out some of my affairs before being admitted to the hospital . . . .

Now you know, Galileo, the reason of my bitterness. I shall never forgive myself for being such a coward . . . . And whenever I hear you talk of Ana, I feel a dagger right through my heart."

"You're just like me, drowning in regrets like a sponge submerged in water. The only difference is that you're young, while I'm . . . Oh, God . . . I guess all that's left for me is to accept

148

whatever comes my way because this might be no more than I
deserve . . . to grope between memory and dream."

LI

"Ana, accompanied by a strange animal, passed close by me
but failed to notice me. Her companion was an enormous butterfly
with obscene wings and blind owl-eyes; because of this, the
butterfly would spin its head in response to the sounds around. I
had made up my mind to go to Alexander's grave on my own if Ana
did not return . . . . While waiting for her, I saw a flock of birds flying
southward. I closed my eyes, and when I opened them again, the
birds were flying in the opposite direction. It may have rained in the
meantime, too, because the earth was damp. It made me feel older
. . . . I realised that Ana was right behind me. She pointed at some
wet pine trees by the side of the road: *See how close to each other
they are and yet how lonely*, she said in a soft voice which I took to
be an attempt at reconciliation. But I was still angry, and I wasn't
going to keep that from her. So I kept silent. *Do you know why
people shake hands?* she asked me. *At first, the gesture had a
particular meaning. People used to shake hands to show the other
that they carried no concealed weapons.* As I was sinking deeper
into my silence, she added: *You must go to the oasis where
Alexander's grave is. There's a round rock behind the straw cottage.
Go there and find out what the oracle has to say to you.* I asked her
to join me. She refused: *You must go alone now*, she said. I could
hear clearly the rustle of each and every pine tree. *I'm just like one
of those animals which have known but one love and are killed by it,*

she continued. In a split second, I could hear the rustling of something other than the pine trees. It can't be true, I thought to myself. But I could instantly see looming through the diaphanous air the dark silhouettes of the eucalyptus trees, the straw cottage, and Alexander's youthful face chiselled in stone, looking up at the sky. Ana's words came to my mind: *Every evening, he would come out of his tent to gaze at the starry sky above. Then he would take a cup of wine, drink the wine, and smash the cup against the rocks.* Beyond the straw cottage, I found the round rock Ana had mentioned. I was presently overcome by an odd tenderness. I stood there for a while listening to the wind, to a bird screaming in the desert, to the rustle of the eucalyptus trees, but just as I was about to leave, the straw cottage caught fire . . . . And that was how it ended. Well, more or less . . . "

"Why 'more or less'?"

"Because I found that my heart was overcome by inexpressible amazement . . . . But tell me about Ignatius of Loyola. Afterwards I'll come back to this."

LII

"When they ordered me to write the 'biography', I didn't know much about him. Only that he had hoped for a military career and wished to die on the battlefield for the second wife of Ferdinand, the Catholic whom he had chosen as the 'queen of his heart'. That a splinter from a cannon ball, which happened to hit him during one of his battles, changed the course of his destiny;

with one leg shorter than the other, he saw his warrior dreams shattered to pieces. And that he founded the order of the Jesuits, finding in religious devotion a new destination for his military principles . . . . That was about all I knew. But after searching through documents, all kinds of intriguing details came to light . . . . While in hospital, he had asked for a book to distract his mind from the pain. They brought him the only books they had in the hospital, 'The Life of Jesus' and a volume of 'The Lives of the Saints'. Whilst reading them, he decided to become a soldier in the army of Christ and the Madonna, and upon leaving the hospital, he went to a Dominican monastery where he frightened the monks with his penances. He would not touch food for days on end and whip himself to kill any desire within. When he started preaching, he took some serious thrashings from fathers and husbands outraged by what that zealot was drumming into the heads of their daughters and wives, for he wished to talk even the prostitutes into following the path of virtue because his understanding of missionary work was beyond rigid. If the Church says that black is black – he would harangue – you must say it is black, even though you can see it is white. He preached poverty and demanded unconditional obedience. To him the Pope was a commander. Ever prone to illness by nature, he would never indulge himself with more than four hours of sleep a night and he put himself through excruciating exercises in the hope of turning himself into a machine in the service of faith."

"I can't pray the same way that I hate. And I'm trying to find God in this world. It's no secret that each morning which arrives with a serene bright sky touches me . . . . I might have exaggerated when I said that I didn't care about anything else except for the light and the cypresses. In fact I do, and yet . . .. "

"Yet?"

"This world can take everything away from me, but it can't take away my right to mourn its loss. More's the pity I cannot bring myself to seeing such losses in simpler terms, too. How can I explain it to you?"

LIII

"... Just like the first time, the inquisitor entered the forester's cabin in the morning, sneered at me, and said, his lips moving but no sound coming out: *Speak up, Galileo, and the snakes will wake up and bite you.* 'But when the candles die out you will speak anyway,' I replied. *Yes, Galileo, you are right, but how do you know that?* 'I've dreamt of you before,' I said. 'I know you.' He gave me a long look. *In that case you know how it all ends?* 'How does it end?' He didn't say anything, only smiled revealing his rotten yellow teeth. 'But what if I'm still dreaming?' I asked. The candles had nearly burnt down. The last drops of tallow were falling down. Suddenly, I saw bizarre shadows looming across the cabin walls. There was a huge stake burning in the courtyard and the wind pairing with the rain stoked up the tall flames. Apart from this, everything else seemed submerged into deep sleep. I tried to fall asleep, too. From time to time, I would wake with a start, but the fire was still ablaze, the morning air was ash-scented, and I wondered how long all this would last. Soon after, the smell of warm milk reached me and I felt relieved. Outside the fire had burnt down the last chunks of wood while the rain was still falling on the warm ash . . . . When I opened my eyes, all I could see were the stars still visible behind the cypress tops, but the rain had been real."

"Summer is almost over. I will leave you in a few days, Galileo."

"As I was lying in bed, I was thinking that. In a way, you are right. Glory is to be found only amongst humans. Cypresses couldn't care less about my discoveries . . . . And that was when, to my astonishment, I understood that perhaps the recantation had raised me up rather than brought me down."

"How so?"

"Before this, I lived with the conviction that I deserved everything, and it never occurred to me that my genius could be limited. What happened to me, however, pulled me out of it and made me human again. The Inquisition is a soul-crushing machine. Standing before it I learnt, together with the fear of death, things I had no knowledge of . . . melancholy, doubt, regret, weakness, despair . . . . It had never dawned on me that one could love desperately and that it is precisely despair which is love's highest token. 'I, Galileo Galilei, aged seventy years, having seen before my eyes all my memories, as tangible to me as stones, I recant the hollow ambitions I indulged in . . . .' What would you say if you heard me talk like this?"

"What are you going to do now?"

"I could return among the humans without detesting them anymore. Why would I ask of them more than they are capable of offering? As I've told you before, unlike Giordano Bruno, I have no intention of reforming the world. I won't change human nature. If someone said: 'Galileo, you recanted', I would answer: 'Yes, I did. What of it? I had no choice. You see to it that you make all inquisitions disappear and then nobody will ever have to recant . . . .' But I don't think this is what I'll choose."

"Now you understand that all I ever expected from you was to accept that everything in the world does concern us."

"I sometimes think of myself as a bell in an abandoned tower which only the wind rings occasionally. Then I can sit and gaze back at my life in peace. But meeting the Inquisition changed me more than I thought it would. And even more than I like to admit."

"I regret to have bothered you, Galileo, but I looked for you because I was convinced that your recantation was not a matter of concern to you alone."

"All you did was to make me look my destiny in the eye and help me realize that one can hope and lose hope using the same words. Do you know what I find particularly sad about my recantation? Not that I recanted, but that I could be forced to recant."

"Julia was stronger than we, Galileo."

"By dying? But should we die in order not to be afraid?"

"Perhaps Julia was in the possession of something that you and I, Galileo, are barely beginning to grasp."

"What would that be?"

"That there is no perfect Inquisition as long as there is one single person left to tell the truth."

"It's not as simple as that. In fact, it's not simple at all. I loved these hills when I didn't know that the day would come when I would need them, but before the Inquisition, I was just a man facing a soul-crushing machine."

"You were more than that, Galileo. You are the dilemma of everyone who is afraid. Or who will one day grow to know fear, having deluded themselves into thinking that they would never know what it is to be threatened."

"I don't know whether I should care about this anymore. What happened changed me. Nothing is as it was before. So I leave to you the truth for which all of you put me on trial. I for one have given it quite enough of my life. Now, I think I'll go look for Ana."

THE END